STAR TREK
THE MODALA IMPERATIVE™

MICHAEL JAN FRIEDMAN
Writer-STAR TREK—The Modala Imperative

PETER DAVID
Writer-STAR TREK: THE NEXT GENERATION™
The Modala Imperative

PABLO MARCOS
Artist

TOM McCRAW
Colorist

BOB PINAHA
Letterer

Original covers by Adam Hughes & Karl Story
Introduction by Walter Koenig

Based on STAR TREK and STAR TREK: THE NEXT GENERATION
created by Gene Roddenberry

STAR TREK—THE MODALA IMPERATIVE

STAR TREK and STAR TREK: THE NEXT GENERATION are registered trademarks of Paramount Pictures.
Published by Titan Books Ltd., 19 Valentine Place, London SE1 8QH, by arrangement with DC Comics Inc. under exclusive license from Paramount Pictures, the trademark owner. Copyright © 1992, Paramount Pictures. All Rights Reserved. Originally published in single magazine form by DC Comics Inc. as: STAR TREK–THE MODALA IMPERATIVE 1-4 and STAR TREK: THE NEXT GENERATION–THE MODALA IMPERATIVE 1-4. Copyright © 1991 Paramount Pictures. All Rights Reserved. The stories, characters, and incidents featured in this publication are entirely fictional.

ISBN #1-85286-457-5
Printed in Canada.
10 9 8 7 6 5 4 3 2 1

Cover painting by Sonia R. Hillios
Publication design by Veronica Carlin

ON SECOND THOUGHT...

Walter Koenig

A Star Trek: The Next Generation television series? Give me a break! I'm justifiably opposed to it on the following grounds:

I. Moral. This is a straightforward case of exploitation. Bad enough to incorporate our title into theirs, but by calling their ship the "Enterprise" they compound the plagiarism. Ethics, where is thy noble visage?

II. Artistic integrity. If the new show doesn't measure up it will cast a pall that will dim the reputation of the original. Have they no conscience?

III. Humanitarian. Think of the fans. Think of their disillusionment. Twenty years of dedication to a superior product and, then, by introducing a pale imitation, reward so contemptuously that loyalty. Betrayal at its most egregious.

Sounds good to me. At least, it did back in 1987 when I was trying to attribute virtue to my umbrage. The last thing I wanted to admit to was proprietary feelings about Star Trek that smacked of puerility. It was only by using the preceding arguments that I was able to obscure from consciousness the image of myself as a pouting child: "If you don't want me to play your game it's because your mother has a moustache"—or something like that. The old sour grapes syndrome at its most acidulous.

My self-righteousness remained intact over the first couple of seasons of Star Trek: The Next Generation. By some strange serendipity (for me) I only happened to catch those episodes in which the series was most patently struggling to find its identity. Bear in mind, we're talking about five programs out of forty-seven. Not a statistically significant sample to be sure, but I wasn't looking for scientifically reliable proof for my prejudice.

Nevertheless, I couldn't help but become aware at Star Trek conventions that the derision of loyalist fans toward the new show that had been so palpable early on, had begun to abate. The quips I made about "Next Gen" began to fall flat. The laugh-o-meter needle barely moved. The forebear wasn't getting the reaction he used to get at the expense of the progeny. It was time to reassess my thinking and take a harder look at both myself and Star Trek: The Next Generation.

What I have with time discovered is a show that stands wholly on its own with no apology to "Classic Trek" and a Walter Koenig who let his territorial feelings about Star Trek cloud his objectivity toward the new series. Wallowing in someone else's failure is character-destructive. Rejoicing in their success is character enriching. I like myself better for liking ST: TNG better.

Which brings me to the happy marriage of both Treks which this book represents. I expected to be interested in the first four issues of The Modala Imperative for obvious reasons. I was delighted, however, to discover that the second half of the story was equally as absorbing.

Popular buzz words in the writer's lexicon are "character-driven" and "plot-driven." The implication is that one cancels out the other. Either the piece is heavy on character and relationship or strong on convolutions of story. They need not be mutually exclusive but as the penchant is to pigeonhole writers (as it is to typecast actors), people who write and the product of their musings are often branded with the one appellation or the other.

It is my happy assignment to state that both Michael Jan Friedman and Peter David have managed to tell absorbing stories with compelling characters. The transition from one writer to the other appeared seamless. The plot, over all eight issues, evolved with pace and surprise, and the dialogue from start to finish was crisp and consistently witty. Would that the films paid as much attention to character speech —particularly among the (ahem) supporting players. Additionally, Pablo Marcos should be complimented on the strong visual impact of all the episodes, and kudos to Bob Pinaha, Tom McCraw and the inestimable Mr. Greenberger for their contributions.

That all said, let's now talk about the singular story artifice that makes this precedent-establishing tome so fundamentally appealing.

We have all, in our lives, either experienced or borne witness to double-crossing, cross bearing, crisscrossing, crossbeaming, cross bunning and cross-dressing. The heart-pounding excitement of the foregoing duly acknowledged, you will concur, I think, that for unadulterated fascination none compares with crossovering. I'm not addressing here transport from this mortal coil but rather the unique literary device that permits one or more heroes from one or more previously independent environments to establish contact with similarly disposed myth-makers from equally disparate spheres of operation. (Look, I'm getting paid by the word!)

I can remember very distinctly and not only cerebrally but, to my embarrassment, viscerally, that Friday at 5:29 on a mid-winter's afternoon in the mid-forties when the announcer for the Superman radio program informed me personally to tune in on the following Monday when Batman and Robin would join Superman in an adventure.

The first time that "cross over" thing happens in your life it is absolutely mind-blowing. If it occurs well before the advent of puberty I'm convinced it is comparable in magnitude to the glory of one's first sexual release.

My God, Batman, Robin and Superman, all together, for a full fifteen minutes fighting injustice in my living room!

Needless to say, never was I so impatient for the heretofore wished-for weekend days of insatiable hedonism to exhaust themselves and the dreaded Monday with Mrs. Seebach and her dreadnaught contours to loom up before me in my second grade class. It was then only a matter of improving my agility at recognizing the passage of time as I assiduously studied the progression of, first, the big hand and, then, the small hand on the classroom wall.

At last, the appointed hour arrived and Batman and Robin did, indeed, join forces with the Man of Steel. Although I no longer remember the story I do know that its denouement was not anticlimactic to my fevered anticipation. This was

definitely not a case of "expectus interruptus." I was fulfilled! I had lived to see the day when superheroes from different worlds linked destinies to combat evil.

For those of you whose interest in the realm of comics doesn't extend beyond Star Trek, let me put it in another perspective: Roosevelt and Churchill, Einstein and Fermi, Thelma and Louise, Robinson and Maglie (they did play together, you know). Whatever, the single most intriguing element in the story you are about to read is the stylishly conceived pairing of two generations of Star Trek heroes. Spock and Picard, in particular, standing back to back defending the faith against the jug-eared pumpkin people (I never said I was steeped in the lore of Next Generation villainy) was a bonding of exhilarating proportions.

And bonding is the operative term. See, dastardly characters don't bond. They only get together for selfish purposes and, consequently, only form a mixture. As every beginning chemistry student knows, you can filter mixtures and separate them, which is, of course, what always happens with the bad

guys: when push comes to shove it's every evil coward for himself.

Bonding, however, reserved fo the pure of heart (now, stay wit me on this) is an organic realign ment, greater than the componer parts, immutable and, therefore inspiring and magical. Hey, don' believe me, just look at the succes of the movie *Twins*! And yo thought it was Danny's selfles charm and Arnold's biting repartee

But, perhaps, I digress.

The cool Captain Picard and th ultra cool Mr. Spock would be a sa isfying tandem under any circum stances, but they become irresistib' when all the significant data ar factored in. (I love techno-babble To begin with, we are not dealin here with heroes whose primar attributes are of a physical nature As a result, we anticipate a battle field less pedestrian than th "BIFF," "POW," "SOCK" in-you face assault suffered by the guy with the bulging muscles. Where the fun in manhandling character not principally known for flyin fists? Far more challenging to attac their strength, their superior mind: and see how they parry and thrus in that arena.

We may not realize going in that that is the nature of the conflict we are in store for but, as is the case very often, well written characters dictate how the story will be told. Without giving conscious shape to our anticipation, we do "sense," then, that these sterling protagonists with their unique talents will demand a story that rises above the ordinary. And, of course, Peter David doesn't let us down. (Sidebar: Say, Mike Friedman, now that we've established a new Star Trek format, how about devising a story that involves plucking some crew members out of the future and settling them down on the Enterprise? Like, maybe, the sensual Deanna Troi interacting with the libidinous Pavel Chekov? Hey, I'm just throwing out ideas here.)

But, perhaps, I digress.

"To you from failing hands we throw the torch, be yours to hold it high."*

The other aspect of The Modala Imperative that makes it inherently interesting involves the concept of legacy. How often in literature have we seen it played out that a warrior comes forth in each succeeding generation to take up the battle with an enduring and indomitable foe? We reserve the word "epic" for such storytelling and immediately assign it an aura of importance. Whereas the enemy actually changes in this book from the Crisaia in the first four chapters to the Ferengi in the final four, the battlefield and its victims, the planet Modala and its inhabitants, remain the same.)

Continuity and progression are staples in this kind of tale. They are story elements that broaden the canvas, making it into a chronicle too vast to play out in a single volume. That, in itself, imbues the work with a sense of weight, the sense of importance previously referred to. The readership is set up to expect more from its scribes. No precise narrative affording instant gratification here but a series of intricately designed unpredictable events steadily moving toward a climax managed by characters who grow and evolve coming into sharper and sharper focus over the breadth of this larger work.

The bridge for all these events, as I said before, is the legacy, the "handing down" of a mission, a task solemnly accepted and valiantly pursued. When this type of story succeeds it is the stuff of legends; when it fails it is just overstuffed.

Although we're talking about Star Trek here and not Homer's *Iliad*, the principle remains intact. It is to the credit of Michael Jan Friedman and Peter David that they invest the legacy story with the epic feeling they strive for and bring it off so entertainingly. The culture of the Modalan people is in jeopardy and, first, Kirk, Chekov and company fight to preserve it and then, eighty years later, Picard, Counselor Troi, *et al.*, accept the same mantle of responsibility. Very well done, indeed.

In a case of life imitating art we should also examine another kind of legacy and, in so doing, properly bookend this piece. *Star Trek VI* has come and gone, having achieved critical success and good domestic box office. Is it time now for its aging crew, once and for all, to "throw the torch" to more supple fingers and amble off into a well-deserved retirement? Jokes about building ramps on the bridge for our wheelchairs notwithstanding, there appears to be ample evidence for a graceful exit of the original troupe. Going out with a "bang" is the best way to go and we certainly did that with our last film. Add to that, that the "Next Generation" show seems to be still on the ascendancy and, in fact, so popular as to spawn its own progeny with a Star Trek: Deep Space 9 television series in the works. All that considered, it's hard to argue for any other course of action.

Look, a part of me would love to see our crew make one more film (not *Star Trek VII*, of course; we'd have to go directly to *Star Trek VIII* since the even numbered movies are the most successful ones) but talent must out, youth must be served. If our band is truly "classic" Trek then we must comport ourselves with class, with dignity. Don't linger, don't dawdle, ride with pride, heads high into the sunset. So long, adios, farewell! The king is dead, long live the king!!

...On the other hand, the foreign box office from the release of *Star Trek VI* appears to be heading for our best ever, somewhere between thirty-five and forty percent of domestic revenue, which would put our tally over one hundred million dollars, showing a profit and, of course, there is still all the *STVI* merchandising to be added in, not to mention the videotapes and the ancillary network television and cable markets and, besides, I still run three miles every other day and eat bran and wear crystals and...

April 10, 1992
No. Hollywood, CA

From the poem "In Flanders Fields" by John McCrae (1872-1918)

YE'D BEST GET SOMETHING STRAIGHT, ENSIGN. THIS IS *NAE* THE BLINKIN' ACADEMY.

WHEN YE MAKE A MISTAKE, IT *COUNTS*.

I MAY *NAE* BE THE *CAPTAIN* SITTING HERE, BUT REST ASSURED-- *HE'D* TELL YE THE *VERRA* SAME THING.

WHEN YE'RE ON THIS BRIDGE, YE'D BETTER BE CONCENTRATIN' ON *BRIDGE* BUSINESS.

OTHERWISE, YE'LL BE OFF THIS SHIP SO FAST YE'LL THINK YE NEVER ARRIVED.

DO I MAKE MYSELF CLEAR, ENSIGN?

AYE, MISTER SCOTT. IT VON'T HAPPEN AGAIN.

A LITTLE SEASONING

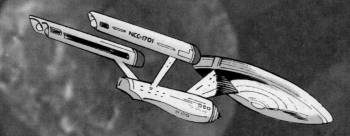

"CAPTAIN'S PERSONAL LOG, STARDATE 3012.4: IT'S BEEN TEN YEARS NOW SINCE I LAST VISITED THE PLANET *MODALA*-- THE NATIVES' NAME FOR BETA DAMORON FIVE.

"OF COURSE, I WAS ONLY A LIEUTENANT THEN, AND *THE ENTERPRISE* WAS SOMEONE ELSE'S SHIP. *CHRIS PIKE'S*, TO BE PRECISE.

NCC-1701

MICHAEL JAN FRIEDMAN • **PABLO MARCOS**
WRITER   ARTIST

BOB   TOM   ROBERT
PINAHA   McCRAW   GREENBERGER
LETTERER   COLORIST   EDITOR

BASED ON *STAR TREK* CREATED BY GENE RODDENBERRY

SPECIAL THANKS TO *RAFAEL GALLUR* FOR ART ASST.

"BACK THEN, I WAS PART OF THE SURVEY TEAM THAT RECOMMENDED MODALA BE CONSIDERED FOR FEDERATION MEMBERSHIP--BUT NOT QUITE YET. I SAID THE MODALANS NEEDED A LITTLE MORE *SEASONING* FIRST.

"AFTER ALL, THEY HAD ALREADY MASTERED SPACEFLIGHT. AND WHILE THEY HADN'T YET RUN INTO ANY STARFARING CIVILIZATIONS, IT WAS ONLY A MATTER OF TIME BEFORE THAT WOULD CHANGE.

"STARFLEET BRASS AGREED. THEY DECIDED THAT MODALA WAS STILL A DECADE AWAY FROM AN INVITATION.

"SO HERE I AM, TEN YEARS LATER, TO CONDUCT A *SECOND* SURVEY, TO SEE IF THE MODALANS HAVE COME AS FAR AS WE EXPECTED THEY WOULD.

"AS BEFORE, OF COURSE, WE'LL WANT TO REMAIN UNOBTRUSIVE. NATIVE GARB AND ALL THAT. OTHERWISE, WE'D BE TAKING A CHANCE ON VIOLATING THE PRIME DIRECTIVE.

"THAT'S WHY IT'LL ONLY BE A TWO-MAN LANDING PARTY. MYSELF--AND ONE OTHER."

BISHOP TO QUEEN'S PAWN TWO, LEVEL ONE.

IF I AM NOT MISTAKEN, THIS WILL BE ENSIGN CHEKOV'S FIRST REAL FIELD EXPERIENCE.

THAT'S CORRECT, MISTER SPOCK.

KNIGHT TAKES BISHOP--I'M OFF TO A GOOD START.

ARE YOU CERTAIN THAT IS WISE, CAPTAIN?

WHAT? TAKING YOUR BISHOP?

NO, I AM REFERRING TO ENSIGN CHEKOV. AFTER ALL, THERE WILL ONLY BE THE *TWO* OF YOU. IF SOMETHING SHOULD GO WRONG...

I APPRECIATE YOUR CONCERN, SPOCK. BUT I'VE BEEN TO MODALA BEFORE, REMEMBER? IT'S NOT EXACTLY THE KLINGON HOMEWORLD.

WHATEVER YOU SAY, CAPTAIN.

INCIDENTALLY, YOUR KING IS IN CHECK.

6

COME IN.

HI. I THOUGHT YOU MIGHT NEED SOMEONE TO TALK TO.

TO TALK TO? VHAT ABOUT?

LISTEN, ENSIGN, YOU'RE NOT THE FIRST GREEN APPLE TO SET FOOT ABOARD A STARSHIP. YOU SHOULD'VE SEEN SOME OF THE KNUCKLEHEAD MOVES *I* PULLED.

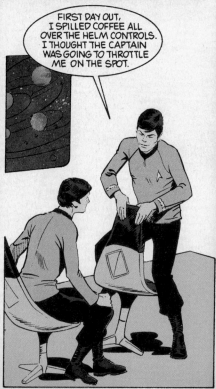

FIRST DAY OUT, I SPILLED COFFEE ALL OVER THE HELM CONTROLS. I THOUGHT THE CAPTAIN WAS GOING TO THROTTLE ME ON THE SPOT.

IF I HAD MY FIRST MISSION AHEAD OF ME, I'D BE NERVOUS, TOO.

NAIRVOUS? WHO'S NAIRVOUS?

YOU ARE. BUT I CAN SEE YOU'RE NEVER GOING TO ADMIT IT.

I GUESS THAT'S OKAY, TOO. LOOK, IF YOU DECIDE TO CHANGE YOUR MIND--

--IT'S NOT TOO DIFFICULT TO FIND ME. NAME'S SULU-- THINK YOU CAN REMEMBER THAT?

SURE-- SULU. I VILL SEE YOU AROUND.

8

READY, MISTER KYLE?

READY, CAPTAIN.

ENERGIZE!

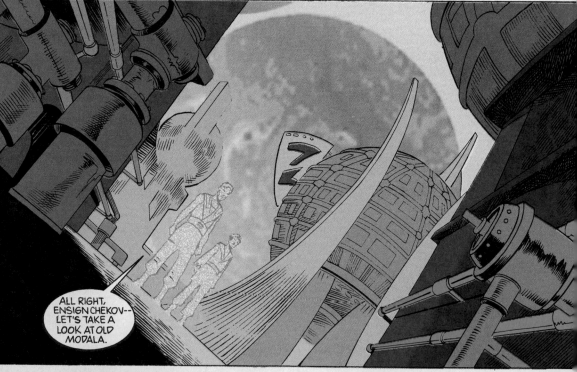

ALL RIGHT, ENSIGN CHEKOV-- LET'S TAKE A LOOK AT OLD MODALA.

IT'S FUNNY, ENSIGN. YOU SEE HUNDREDS OF PLANETS, BUT ONLY A FEW STICK IN YOUR MIND. THIS IS ONE OF THE ONES THAT STUCK.

VHY IS THAT, KEPTIN?

I DON'T KNOW, EXACTLY. IT WAS SORT OF PLEASANT HERE. THERE WAS A SPIRIT OF PROGRESS-- OF OPTIMISM.

A SOCIETY ON THE BRINK OF A GREAT ADVENTURE-- ABOUT TO TAKE TO THE STARS.

KEPTIN...

THINGS HAVE CHANGED AROUND HERE, ALL RIGHT. BUT *NOT* FOR THE BETTER.

ALL RIGHT-- YOU KNOW THE RULES. NO ASSEMBLIES.

BUT I WAS JUST ASKING DIRECTIONS...

THAT'S WHAT THEY ALL SAY. NOW *MOVE!*

I TOLD YOU TO DISPERSE, DIDN'T I?

NO... PLEASE...

UNNH!

WHERE THE BLAZES DID *YOU* COME FROM?

ACTUALLY, DOCTOR, IT IS PERFECTLY LOGICAL TO HAVE JUNIOR OFFICERS ACCOMPANY MORE SEASONED PERSONNEL ON AWAY MISSIONS.

HOW ELSE CAN THEY GAIN EXPERIENCE?

BY STARTING OUT SMALL-- DOING SURVEYS OF BAR- REN ROCKS, *THEN* THEY CAN GRADUATE TO POPULATED PLANETS-- AFTER THEY'VE SLOGGED THROUGH A FEW CORIAN FOURS AND BLISTERED THEIR FEET ON SOME NAKRAZUT SEVENS.

APPARENTLY, THE CAPTAIN DISAGREES.

YOU'RE JUST RATIONALIZING BECAUSE YOU WEREN'T ASKED TO COME ALONG. IF YOU *HAD* BEEN, YOU WOULDN'T HAVE HESITATED FOR A MINUTE.

IN FACT, I WOULDN'T BE SURPRISED IF YOU TRIED TO TALK HIM *OUT* OF TAKING THIS ENSIGN WHATHISNAME-- AND FAILED!

I DID NO SUCH THING, DOCTOR. NOW IF YOU WILL PARDON ME, I SHOULD BE GETTING UP TO THE BRIDGE.

PSHAW! SOUNDS LIKE SOUR GRAPES TO ME!

14

WHAT HAPPENED TO THE WOMAN?

SHE RAN OFF. DIDN'T VANT TO BE CAUGHT CONGREGATING AGAIN.

THESE PEOPLE ARE SCARED HALF TO DEATH, KEPTIN. VHAT COULD HAVE HAPPENED HERE TO CHANGE THIS PLACE SO?

HARD TO SAY, ENSIGN. SOMETIMES IT'S NOT ONE THING, BUT A *SERIES* OF THINGS.

OF COURSE, THERE'S ONLY *ONE* WAY TO REALLY KNOW--AND THAT'S TO CARRY OUR INVESTIGATION A LITTLE FURTHER.

IT VON'T BE EASY, SAIR. WITH THE MODALANS TOO SCARED TO TALK TO US, INFORMATION WILL BE DIFFICULT TO COME BY.

THERE'S ONE THING YOU SHOULD KNOW ABOUT TYRANNICAL REGIMES, ENSIGN--THEY BREED OPPOSITION.

SOMEONE WILL TALK TO US. IT'S JUST A MATTER OF *FINDING* THEM...

FIRST THEIR FILTHY MINISTRY OF ORDER-- AND THEN THE POLICE THEMSELVES!

BUDDA-BUDDA!

JOIN US! THROW OFF YOUR CHAINS AND STRIKE BACK!

DON'T LOOK NOW, KEPTIN--BUT I THINK VE HAVE *FOUND* THE *OPPOSITION.*

"YES, ENSIGN. AND SO HAVE THE POLICE."

SAIR--THOSE VEAPONS THE POLICE ARE FIRING--

"--THEY DON'T BELONG ON THIS WORLD. THEY'RE MUCH TOO *ADVANCED!*"

17

ZZT BLAM!

YOU ALL RIGHT, ENSIGN?

TO BE HONEST, SAIR, I HAVE FELT BETTER.

WHERE DO YOU THINK *YOU'RE* GOING?

REBEL SCUM!

CONTACT THE CAPTAIN IMMEDIATELY, UHURA.

WHAT SORT OF DISTURBANCES, LIEUTENANT?

I'M NOT SURE, SIR. BUT THEY *COULD* BE *EXPLOSIONS.*

MISTER SPOCK-- I'M PICKING UP SOME DISTURBANCES IN THE IMMEDIATE VICINITY OF THE BEAM-DOWN SITE.

TRYING, SIR.

THE CAPTAIN'S COMMUNICATOR IS OPERATIONAL--BUT HE DOESN'T ANSWER. SHOULD I KEEP TRYING, MISTER SPOCK?

NO, LIEUTENANT-- NOT IMMEDIATELY. IF THE CAPTAIN IS NOT ANSWERING, IT MAY BE HE HAS HIS *REASONS.*

20

WHAT WAS *THAT?*

ER... WHAT WAS WHAT?

THAT BEEPING. IT CAME FROM INSIDE YOUR SHIRT.

FROM INSIDE... MY SHIRT? ARE YOU SURE?

KEPTIN... THE PRIME DIRECTIVE...

UNHH!

WAS THAT REALLY NECESSARY?

THAT'S WHAT HE GETS FOR *WHISPERING.*

AND UNLESS YOU WANT THE SAME--OR *WORSE*--YOU'LL HAND OVER WHATEVER IT IS YOU'VE GOT IN YOUR SHIRT!

21

YOU WANT IT? WELL, THEN—

—HERE IT IS!

CLIK!

FLAT!

KRUNNCH!

YOU'RE GOING TO WISH YOU HADN'T DONE THAT.

I HAD NO CHOICE IN THE MATTER. NOTHING PERSONAL.

TAKE THEM AWAY! I'LL DEAL WITH HIM LATER!

"MISTER SPOCK-- I'M NO LONGER GETTING A SIGNAL FROM THE CAPTAIN'S COMMUNICATOR! IT'S GONE DEAD!"

ARE YOU CERTAIN ABOUT THAT, LIEUTENANT?

ABSOLUTELY, SIR. EITHER THERE'S A MALFUNCTION OR...

YOU NEED NOT RECITE THE ALTERNATIVE, LIEUTENANT. THANK YOU.

DID I JUST HEAR CORRECTLY, SPOCK? HAS SOMETHING HAPPENED TO THE CAPTAIN?

THAT HAS YET TO BE DETERMINED, DOCTOR. FOR THE TIME BEING, ALL WE KNOW IS THAT SOMETHING HAS HAPPENED TO HIS COMMUNICATOR.

WELL, THAT'S ALMOST THE SAME THING, ISN'T IT? THE POINT IS, THEY'RE IN TROUBLE DOWN THERE.

24

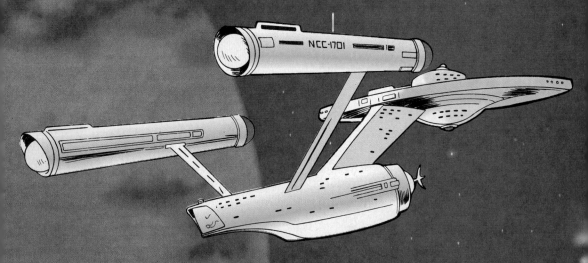

TOOLS OF TYRANNY

THE QUESTION BEFORE US IS NOT AS EASY AS IT SEEMS, GENTLEMEN.

MICHAEL JAN FRIEDMAN
WRITER

PABLO MARCOS
ARTIST

BOB PINAHA
LETTERER

TOM McCRAW
COLORIST

ROBERT GREENBERGER
TOUR GUIDE

BASED ON
STAR TREK
CREATED BY
GENE RODDENBERRY

WHAT ARE YOU TALKING ABOUT, SPOCK? JIM AND ENSIGN CHEKOV ARE IN SOME KIND OF TROUBLE DOWN THERE-- IT'S AS PLAIN AS THE NOSE ON YOUR FACE!

I DO NOT DISPUTE THAT, DOCTOR. HOWEVER, THERE ARE OTHER ASPECTS OF THE SITUATION WHICH WE MUST TAKE INTO ACCOUNT.

FOR INSTANCE, THE MATTER OF THE PRIME DIRECTIVE. AS YOU KNOW, WE ARE FORBIDDEN FROM INTERFERING IN THE DEVELOPMENT OF OTHER CULTURES AND CIVILIZATIONS.

OF *COURSE* WE KNOW THAT. GET TO THE POINT, SPOCK.

MODALA IS A DEVELOPING CULTURE. BY SENDING DOWN TWO OF OUR PEOPLE, HOWEVER DISCREETLY, WE MAY ALREADY HAVE AFFECTED THAT CULTURE.

THE CAPTAIN WOULD NEVER VIOLATE THE DIRECTIVE, MISTER SPOCK. SURELY YE KNOW THAT.

THE CAPTAIN WOULD NEVER DO SO *KNOWINGLY*-- I AGREE. BUT IF HE IS IN TROUBLE, AS DOCTOR McCOY SUGGESTS, THEN HE MAY NOT BE ABLE TO HELP IT.

2

BEGGIN' YER PARDON, SIR... BUT IF YOU PLANNED TO SEND DOWN A RESCUE TEAM ALL ALONG--THEN WHAT WAS THE POINT OF THIS MEETING?

I VALUE YOUR OPINIONS, COMMANDER. THE FACT THAT I HAD MADE A DECISION ALREADY DID NOT MEAN I COULD NOT HAVE BEEN DISSUADED FROM IT-- PROVIDED THE ARGUMENT WAS COMPELLING ENOUGH.

VERY SENSIBLE, SPOCK.

THANK YOU, DOCTOR.

SO WHAT ARE WE WAITING FOR? LET'S GO FIND THE CAPTAIN.

"WE" IS AN INAPPROPRIATE PRONOUN, DOCTOR McCOY. I WILL BE BEAMING DOWN ALONE.

WHAT?

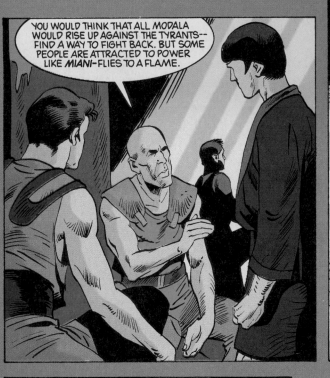

YOU WOULD THINK THAT ALL MODALA WOULD RISE UP AGAINST THE TYRANTS-- FIND A WAY TO FIGHT BACK. BUT SOME PEOPLE ARE ATTRACTED TO POWER LIKE *MIANI*--FLIES TO A FLAME.

BUT THE SITUATION CAN'T BE HOPELESS. YOU FIGHT BACK, DON'T YOU?

AS BEST WE CAN. BUT LOOK WHERE IT'S GOTTEN US.

OUR LEADER, TILLIS, IS DEAD. SOME OF THE OTHERS AS WELL.

AND HALF OF THOSE WHO STILL LIVE ARE ROTTING AWAY IN THIS PRISON.

VELL, VE KNOW MORE THAN VE DID BEFORE.

BUT NOT ENOUGH.

WE STILL DON'T KNOW HOW THE KRISAIA GOT THOSE WEAPONS.

6

IT IS SIMPLY THAT I WISH TO MINIMIZE THE RISK OF FURTHER CONTAMINATION. SURELY YOU CAN UNDERSTAND THAT, DOCTOR.

WE'RE NOT TALKING ABOUT THE WHOLE CREW HERE, SPOCK--JUST YOU AND ME. I MEAN, WHAT IF JIM AND CHEKOV NEED A DOCTOR?

THEN WE WILL BEAM THEM UP TO SICKBAY, WHERE THEY CAN BE TREATED PROPERLY. THAT WOULD SEEM TO BE THE LOGICAL STRATEGY.

AND WHAT IF *YOU* GET HURT? WHO'S GOING TO BE AROUND TO HAVE *YOU* BEAMED UP?

MY SAFETY IS NOT THE FOREMOST CONCERN HERE. THE PRIME DIRECTIVE *IS*.

WHAT KIND OF HAPPY HORSEBLEEP IS *THAT*? IF YOU WANT TO BE A MARTYR, SPOCK, JUST SAY SO!

I DO NOT WISH TO BE A MARTYR, DOCTOR. I AM SIMPLY TRYING TO CARRY OUT MY DUTIES IN THE MOST LOGICAL WAY POSSIBLE.

JUST REMEMBER WHO YOU'LL BE LEAVING IN CHARGE HERE, SPOCK. AFTER ALL, I'LL BE THE HIGHEST-RANKING OFFICER LEFT ON THE SHIP.

NOT IF I SPECIFICALLY PLACE MISTER SCOTT IN CHARGE.

MISTER SCOTT CAN BE RELIEVED OF COMMAND BY THE SHIP'S SURGEON-- JUST LIKE ANY-BODY ELSE.

THIS IS CHILDISH AND CAPRICIOUS, DOCTOR. COMMAND DECISIONS SHOULD NOT BE BASED ON IRRATIONALITY.

YOU MEAN LIKE THE IRRATIONALITY OF GOING DOWN THERE *ALONE*?

WHAT HAPPENED TO WHAT YOU SAID IN THE CONFERENCE ROOM? IF A SECOND OPINION WAS VALUABLE TO YOU *THEN*, WOULDN'T IT BE *TWICE* AS VALUABLE PLANET-SIDE?

FOR A BASICALLY ILLOGICAL BEING, DOCTOR, YOU CAN BE ANNOYINGLY *LOGICAL* AT TIMES.

8

NOT THE **WORST** GRUEL I'VE EVER TASTED, I SUPPOSE.

YOU'VE BEEN IN THIS SITUATION BEFORE?

YOU MEAN TOSSED INTO PRISON? ONLY ABOUT AS MANY TIMES AS I HAVE FINGERS--AND TOES.

VELL, **THAT** IS A RELIEF. THERE MUST BE SOMEONE **ELSE** ON THE SHIP AS INEPT AS I AM.

INEPT? I'M AFRAID I DON'T UNDERSTAND, ENSIGN.

THAT IS KIND OF YOU TO SAY SO, SAIR. BUT I'M SAIRTAIN THAT IF MISTER SPOCK HAD BEEN VITH YOU, OR DOCTOR McCOY, YOU VOULD NOT BE **IN** THIS MESS.

DON'T COMPARE YOURSELF WITH MISTER SPOCK, ENSIGN. HE'S IN A CLASS BY HIMSELF.

AND AS FOR DOCTOR McCOY... WELL, I GUESS HE IS TOO, IN A WAY.

BUT THOSE TWO ARE SEASONED OFFICERS. NOBODY--NOT EVEN SPOCK-- IS BORN WITH A KNACK FOR PLANET-ARY MISSIONS.

9

BUT IT'S NOT JUST PLANETARY MISSIONS I'M INEPT AT, SAIR. JUST YESTERDAY, I VAS REPRIMANDED BY COMMANDER SCOTT--FOR DAYDREAMING.

AND THE DAY BEFORE, ON A ROUTINE MAINTENANCE DETAIL, I ALMOST OPENED THE WRONG AIRLOCK. I COULD'VE GOTTEN MYSELF KILLED!

YOU'VE JUST GOT TO CALM DOWN, ENSIGN. STOP TAKING EVERYTHING SO SERIOUSLY.

YOU'RE SUPPOSED TO RETURN THOSE PLATES--NOT MAKE ME COME AND GET THEM!

OOMPH!

NOBODY DOES THAT TO JAMES T. KIRK!

STOP RIGHT THERE--OR I'LL FRY YOU BOTH!

UNNH!

10

NO MORE! WE GET THE IDEA!

SEE THAT YOU DO! ONE MORE STUNT LIKE THAT AND I WON'T BE SO LENIENT!

"NOBODY DOES THAT TO JAMES T. KIRK"? I'VE HEARD OF BEING PROTECTIVE, BUT...

...COULD ENSIGN CHEKOV HAVE A TOUCH OF HERO WORSHIP?

THAT WOULD EXPLAIN HIS TRYING TOO HARD--AND THE WAY HE COMES DOWN ON HIMSELF WHEN HE FAILS.

HE'S TRYING TO LIVE UP TO MY REPUTATION--JUST AS I TRIED TO LIVE UP TO CAPTAIN GARTH'S WHEN I WAS AT THE ACADEMY.

BUT I DIDN'T HAVE THE ADDED PRESSURE OF SERVING UNDER GARTH--AS CHEKOV IS SERVING UNDER ME.

11

12

CAREFUL, BROTHER. NO TALKING-- IT WILL ONLY DRAW ATTENTION TO YOU.

THEN YOU'LL BE PART OF THE CLEAN-UP CREW. OR WORSE.

WHAT ARE THEY CLEANING UP, ANYWAY?

DIDN'T YOU HEAR IT? THE REBELS SET OFF A BOMB.

THAT WOULD EXPLAIN THE DISTURBANCES UHURA PICKED UP.

UNFORTUNATELY, IT MAY ALSO EXPLAIN THE CAPTAIN'S DISAPPEARANCE.

SPOCK-- YOU DON'T THINK--?

THAT THE CAPTAIN AND ENSIGN CHEKOV WERE KILLED IN THE BOMB BLAST?

HOWEVER UNFORTUNATE, DOCTOR, IT IS A DISTINCT POSSIBILITY.

CHRISTINE?

DIDN'T YOU JUST CHECK THAT DISPLAY A COUPLE OF HOURS AGO?

I GUESS I DID, DOCTOR M'BENGA BUT IT KEEPS ME BUSY--IF YOU KNOW WHAT I MEAN.

IT'S HARD WAITING UP HERE WHILE THEY GO GALLAVANTING DOWN THERE.

YES-- DAMNED HARD.

BUT YOU ALWAYS SEEM SO CALM. WHAT'S YOUR SECRET?

IT'S NO SECRET AT ALL.

I SPENT A COUPLE OF YEARS TREATING VULCANS. IF THEY CAN'T TEACH YOU DETACHMENT, NO ONE CAN.

15

YOU SEE HOW WE ARE TREATED--LIKE ANIMALS! LIKE FILTH!

LET THESE TWO BE OUR INSPIRATION! DESPITE THE BRUTALITY OF THE POLICE, THEIR SPIRITS HAVE REMAINED UNDAUNTED.

IF WE EVER GET OUT OF HERE, I PROMISE YOU-- THE STREETS WILL RUN *RED* WITH KRISAIAN BLOOD!

CAN I SAY SOMETHING?

BY ALL MEANS, SPEAK!

I THINK YOU MAY BE GOING ABOUT THIS THE WRONG WAY. IT'S NOT NECESSARY TO *KILL* IN ORDER TO FIGHT BACK.

BLOODSHED IS *THEIR* GAME--THE GAME OF THE TYRANTS. YOU CAN'T BEAT THEM AT IT.

16

LET'S JUST SAY I'VE SEEN THESE THINGS DONE--AND I KNOW THEY WORK BETTER THAN SPILLING BLOOD IN THE STREETS.

AN INTERESTING APPROACH. WE'LL HAVE TO TRY IT--IF WE EVER GET THE CHANCE.

CONGRATULATIONS, SAIR. IT SEEMS YOU'VE PUT THE REVOLUTION ON A WHOLE NEW FOOTING.

I HOPE SO, ENSIGN.

WE CAN'T ACTUALLY AID THEM IN THEIR FIGHT-- BUT WE CAN HELP TO KEEP THE BODY COUNT DOWN.

AND YOU DID IT VITHOUT GIVING US AVAY. A MASTERFUL JOB, KEPTIN.

NOTHING YOU COULDN'T HAVE DONE YOURSELF, ENSIGN. ALL IT TAKES IS A LITTLE CHUTZPAH.

CHUTZPAH, KEPTIN?

MISTER SCOTT?

I HEAR YE, COMMANDER. GO AHEAD, SIR.

UNFORTUNATELY, WE HAVE BEEN UNABLE TO OBTAIN ANY INFORMATION ON THE CAPTAIN AND ENSIGN CHEKOV. AND WHAT WE HAVE LEARNED ABOUT CURRENT EVENTS ON MODALA HAS NOT HELPED TO SET OUR MINDS AT EASE.

IT DOES NAE SOUND GOOD, SIR.

NO, MISTER SCOTT, IT DOES NOT.

WHAT ABOUT YERSELVES? YE'RE NOT IN ANY TROUBLE, ARE YE?

NOT AT THE PRESENT TIME-- THOUGH WE HAVE LEARNED FROM EXPERIENCE THAT THAT CAN CHANGE FROM MOMENT TO MOMENT.

IN THE MEANTIME, WE WILL PROCEED WITH OUR SEARCH. DOCTOR McCOY HAS FOUND A PLACE WHERE HE BELIEVES WE MAY LEARN SOMETHING.

"SPOCK OUT."

NCC-1701

COME ON, SPOCK. THE PLACE IS JUST FILLING UP.

WE ARE TAKING QUITE A CHANCE, DOCTOR.

NONSENSE, SPOCK. IF YOU WANT ANONYMITY, LOOK FOR A CROWD.

Tavern

DAMN. I'VE SEEN UNRULIER MOBS IN A TURBOLIFT.

JUST FOLLOW ME, SPOCK. I KNOW MY WAY AROUND PLACES LIKE THESE.

I HAVE NO DOUBT OF IT, DOCTOR.

THE FIRST THING WE DO IS FIND THE BARTENDER. IF ANYBODY KNOWS ANYTHING AROUND HERE, IT'LL BE HIM.

CAN I GET YOU SOMETHING?

SEE, SPOCK? THESE PLACES ARE THE SAME ALL OVER.

20

THE POOR KID...

DID YOU SAY SOMETHING, SULU?

I WAS THINKING ABOUT CHEKOV, LESLIE.

OH--RIGHT. HELL OF A WAY TO BREAK IN, ISN'T IT?

HE GOES OFF ON WHAT SEEMS LIKE THE EASIEST MISSION EVER--AND WINDS UP MISSING IN ACTION.

DON'T BE COUNTIN' HIM OUT QUITE YET, LADDIE BUCK THAT CHEKOV IS A DAMNED FINE MAN. TOP-NOTCH OFFICER MATERIAL.

HE'LL FIND A WAY OUT O' THIS MESS--WITH THE CAPTAIN'S HELP, OF COURSE.

AND YE DINNA NEED TO REMIND ME O' HOW I LACED INTO HIM. THAT WAS FOR A REASON-- TO TOUGHEN HIM UP FER AN OCCASION JUST LIKE THIS ONE.

NOW, NO MORE TALK O' DOOM AND GLOOM--OR I'LL TELL CHEKOV O' YER LACK O' FAITH WHEN HE GETS BACK!

22

DOCTOR, YOU SPECIFICALLY SAID THAT--

I KNOW WHAT I SAID, SPOCK.

STATISTICALLY SPEAKING, BARTENDERS DO KNOW EVERYTHING. WE JUST HAPPENED TO PICK ON THE EXCEPTION THAT PROVES THE RULE.

PERHAPS WE SHOULD TRY AN ALTERNATIVE PLAN.

FINE, SPOCK. YOU COME UP WITH ONE--I'M ALL OUT.

IT SEEMS TO ME WE'VE BUTTONHOLED EVERYONE IN THIS PLACE--AND THEN SOME. IF WE DRAW ANY MORE ATTENTION TO OURSELVES, PEOPLE WILL START TO WONDER WHERE WE'RE REALLY FROM.

...PERHAPS I CAN HELP YOU FIND THOSE YOU'RE LOOKING FOR.

EXCUSE ME, BROTHERS...

23

THE PRICE OF FREEDOM

I SEE NOW WHAT OUR INFORMANT MEANT WHEN SHE SAID THIS PLACE WAS IMPREGNABLE. BY MODALAN STANDARDS, IT IS.

MICHAEL JAN FRIEDMAN
WRITER

PABLO MARCOS
ARTIST

BOB PINAHA
LETTERER

TOM McCRAW
COLORIST

ROBERT GREENBERGER
EDITOR

BASED ON STAR TREK
CREATED BY
GENE RODDENBERRY

MISTER SCOTT?

AYE, COMMANDER. I'VE BEEN *WAITIN'* TO HEAR FROM YOU.

WE HAVE NARROWED DOWN THE LOCATIONS OF CAPTAIN KIRK AND ENSIGN CHEKOV CONSIDERABLY.

MISTER KYLE WILL BE GLAD TO HEAR *THAT*, SIR. HE'S BEEN WORKIN' HIS TAIL OFF TRYIN' TO FIND THEM IN THAT MESS O' MODALANS.

EXACTLY WHERE DO YE THINK THE CAPTAIN AND CHEKOV *ARE*?

IT APPEARS TO BE A *PRISON*, MISTER SCOTT.

MAKE THAT A *LARGE* PRISON, SPOCK. A *VERY* LARGE PRISON.

WHAT WAS THAT, MISTER SPOCK?

NOTHING OF CONSEQUENCE. I AM TRANSMITTING COORDINATES NOW.

MISTER SCOTT, I'M RECEIVING THE COORDINATES. THEY'RE APPROXIMATELY TEN KILOMETERS FROM THE BEAM-DOWN SITE.

2

OUR OLD LEADER IS DEAD. WE NEED SOMEONE NEW. SOMEONE WHO IS NOT AFRAID.

YOU ARE THE ONE WHO SHOWED US HOW TO STAND UP TO THE POLICE. YOU ARE THE ONE WHO SAID YOU HAD SEEN WAYS TO STOP THEIR OPPRESSION.

WHAT BETTER CHOICE COULD WE MAKE? YOU MUST LEAD US!

I'M GLAD I'VE BEEN OF SOME HELP TO YOU--BUT I THINK YOU'RE MAKING A MISTAKE.

KNOWING WHAT TO DO AND DOING IT ARE TWO DIFFERENT THINGS. AND A LEVEL HEAD IS MORE IMPORTANT THAN A LITTLE BRAVADO.

OF COURSE, IF YOU DON'T MIND A SUGGESTION...

5

ANY LUCK WI' THOSE COORDINATES, MISTER KYLE?

ACTUALLY, COMMANDER, THEY'VE BEEN QUITE HELPFUL.

I'VE LOCATED A LARGE CONCENTRATION OF MODALANS THAT MIGHT REPRESENT A PRISON POPULATION. IF MISTER SPOCK WAS RIGHT, AND THEY'RE IN THERE, IT SHOULD ONLY BE A MATTER OF TIME BEFORE I FIND THEM.

THE PROBLEM IS--

I KNOW, LADDIE. YE DINNA HAVE TO TELL ME.

THE MODALANS ARE DEAD RINGERS FOR US HUMANS, DOWN TO TH' CONFIGURATION OF THEIR INTERNAL ORGANS. IN FACT, YE'VE GOT T' WONDER IF THEY'RE NOT SOMEHOW AN OFFSHOOT OF TH' HUMAN RACE.

"UNFORTUNATELY, THEIR SIMILARITY T' HUMANS MAKES IT DIFFICULT T' FIND THE CAPTAIN AND ENSIGN CHEKOV AMONG THEM. WE'VE GOT T' DEPEND ON TH' SUBTLETIES O' THEIR BIO-PROFILES IN ORDER T' PINPOINT THEIR LOCATIONS."

YOU KNOW, SPOCK, WE'VE BEEN HERE FOR HOURS AND YOU STILL HAVEN'T TOLD ME I WAS RIGHT.

RIGHT ABOUT *WHAT*, DOCTOR?

ABOUT ME COMING ALONG, OF COURSE. NOW, YOU'VE GOT TO ADMIT IT--WITHOUT MY INSISTENCE ON GOING INTO THAT TAVERN, WE MIGHT *STILL* BE WITHOUT A CLUE AS TO JIM'S WHEREABOUTS.

NEED I REMIND YOU, DOCTOR MCCOY, THAT MISTER KYLE HAS SO FAR FAILED TO LOCATE THE CAPTAIN? OR THAT OUR ONLY SOURCE OF INFORMATION IN THIS MATTER IS A WOMAN WHO HAS YET TO PROVE HERSELF RELIABLE?

COME ON, SPOCK. YOU HEARD HER DESCRIBE THE CAPTAIN AND CHEKOV.

IT IS NOT HER ABILITY TO IDENTIFY THEM THAT TROUBLES ME. IT IS HER ABILITY TO PREDICT WHERE THE AUTHORITIES HAVE TAKEN THEM.

HOW MANY PRISONS LIKE *THIS* COULD THERE BE AROUND HERE?

A TOTALITARIAN REGIME MIGHT HAVE NEED FOR *MANY* LARGE PRISONS, DOCTOR. IT IS THE NATURE OF SUCH REGIMES TO LOOK AT *EVERY-ONE* AS A POTENTIAL PRISONER.

"AND THOSE WEAPONS WE SAW WOULD GIVE THE TYRANTS THE UPPER HAND IN ANY CONFRONTATION. THE NUMBER OF PRISONERS--AND THE NEED FOR PRISONS TO HOUSE THEM-- WOULD BE DIRECTLY PROPORTIONAL TO THE DEGREE OF RESISTANCE AMONG THE MODALANS."

BLAST! LEAVE IT TO YOU, SPOCK, TO MAKE OPPRESSION SOUND LIKE A MATHEMATICAL EQUATION.

AS A FORM OF LOGIC, MATHEMATICS IS A VALID MEANS OF ANALYSIS, DOCTOR.

THAT'S *RIDICULOUS!* HOW CAN MATHEMATICS EXPRESS MOTIVATIONS? EMOTIONS?

WITH GREAT PRECISION--THROUGH STATISTICAL MODELS. WHICH, IF I AM NOT MISTAKEN, HAVE BEEN IN USE AMONG HUMANS FOR THE LAST THREE HUNDRED YEARS.

9

IT'S BEEN MY EXPERIENCE THAT LEADERS ARE BEST WHEN THEY COME FROM WITHIN--NOT SOMEONE LIKE ME, WHOM YOU HARDLY KNOW.

THIS MAN HAS SHOWN ME COURAGE AND DETERMINATION. HE HAS SHOWN ME A WILLINGNESS TO ADOPT THE NEW METHODS I SPOKE OF.

IF IT WERE MY CHOICE, THIS MAN WOULD BE YOUR NEW LEADER!

STROYKA? BUT HE'S SO YOUNG!

MEASURED IN YEARS, YES-- HE IS YOUNG. BUT YOU'VE FOUGHT ALONG-SIDE HIM. YOU KNOW THAT HE'S SEEN AS MUCH AS MEN TWICE HIS AGE.

MORE IMPORTANT, HE WAS ONE WHO SPOKE UP WHEN THE REST OF YOU HAD ACCEPTED YOUR IMPRISONMENT.

HE WAS ONE WHO TOOK THE INITIATIVE!

10

IN FACT, I SUBMIT TO YOU THAT HE IS *ALREADY* YOUR LEADER. YOU JUST DON'T KNOW IT YET!

KIRK'S WORD IS GOOD ENOUGH FOR ME. I SAY WE FOLLOW STROYKA!

AND I AS WELL!

VERY INTERESTING, SAIR. BUT DO YOU THINK HE IS REALLY CAPABLE OF LEADING THE REVOLUTION?

WHY NOT, MISTER CHEKOV?

DON'T TELL ME *YOU'RE* GOING TO HOLD HIS AGE AGAINST HIM, TOO. YOU'D BE SURPRISED AT WHAT YOUNG PEOPLE CAN DO GIVEN HALF A CHANCE

STROYKA'S GOING TO MAKE HIS SHARE OF MISTAKES, NO DOUBT. BUT HE AND HIS PEOPLE WILL SURVIVE THEM.

THE IMPORTANT THING IS FOR HIM NOT TO LOSE HIS CONFIDENCE. TO PUT HIS MISTAKES ASIDE AND GO ON.

AND THAT'S SOMETHING THAT CAN'T BE TAUGHT, ENSIGN. IT HAS TO BE *INSIDE* A PERSON.

11

LOOK--THE
PRISONERS!

QUICKLY--
HEAD FOR THE
GATE!

ARRH!

CHEKOV!

WHAT THE...? DAMN!

MISTER SCOTT!

AYE, CHIEF! WHAT IS IT?

"I'VE LOST THEIR COORDINATES, SIR! SOMETHING HAPPENED DOWN THERE--AND IN THE CONFUSION, I *LOST* THEM!"

IT'S ALL RIGHT, KYLE. YE'LL FIND THEM AGAIN--I KNOW YE WILL.

MAYBE THE LANDING PARTY KNOWS WHAT HAPPENED.

19

MISTER SPOCK? WE'VE LOST THE CAPTAIN'S COORDINATES. IS SOMETHIN' GOIN' ON DOWN THERE?

MISTER SPOCK? COME IN, PLEASE.

LIEUTENANT?

HIS COMMUNICATOR'S WORKING, COMMANDER. HE'S JUST NOT ANSWERING.

MISTER KYLE-- HAVE YE STILL GOT A FIX ON SPOCK AND McCOY?

I DO, SIR. SHALL I BEAM THEM UP?

NOT YET, CHIEF. BUT I'LL KEEP YE POSTED.

DAMN.

FUSSH FUSSH FUSSH

SPOCK...
WHAT'S GOING
ON...?

SPOCK...?

GET YOUR HANDS *UP*.

AT LEAST WE CAUGHT A *COUPLE* OF THEM. THAT SHOULD PACIFY THE CHIEF A *LITTLE*.

WE'LL CATCH THE OTHERS, TOO. IT'LL JUST TAKE SOME TIME.

WE'RE NOT WHO YOU *THINK* WE ARE. WE WEREN'T PRISONERS.

THAT'S WHAT THEY *ALL* SAY.

SPOCK-- YOUR COMMUNICATOR. DID YOU DITCH IT?

UNFORTUNATELY, DOCTOR, I DID *NOT*.

SPOCK...IF THEY FIND THAT COMMUNICATOR...IT'LL BLOW A HOLE IN THE PRIME DIRECTIVE... MAYBE EVEN *BIGGER* THAN THE ONE THOSE WEAPONS HAVE MADE...

I KNOW, DOCTOR. I *KNOW*.

FOR WHOM THE BELL TOLLS

MICHAEL JAN FRIEDMAN
WRITER

PABLO MARCOS
ARTIST

BOB PINAHA
LETTERER

TOM McCRAW
COLORIST

ROBERT GREENBERGER
EDITOR

BASED ON STAR TREK CREATED BY GENE RODDENBERRY

"SAIR! IT'S MISTER SPOCK! AND DOCTOR McCOY!"

"I CAN SEE THAT, ENSIGN."

MAYBE VE CAN JUMP THE GUARDS-- GET THEIR VEAPONS--

THERE ARE TOO MANY OF THEM. WE WOULDN'T HAVE A CHANCE--AND WE WOULD BE ENDANGERING THE PRISONERS.

VE HAVE TO DO SOMETHING!

YES.

BUT RIGHT NOW, OUR BEST COURSE OF ACTION IS TO REJOIN THE REBELS.

I THOUGHT YOU SAID VE HAD MEDDLED ENOUGH?

THE SITUATION HAS CHANGED SOMEWHAT. WE NEED HELP.

AND OUR FRIENDS THE REBELS ARE THE ONLY ONES WE CAN DEPEND ON.

③

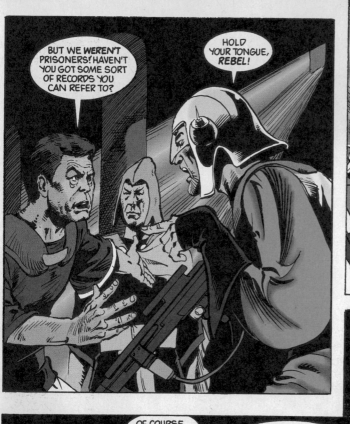

BUT WE WEREN'T PRISONERS! HAVEN'T YOU GOT SOME SORT OF RECORDS YOU CAN REFER TO?

HOLD YOUR TONGUE, REBEL!

IF YOU WERE NOT ESCAPING, WHAT WERE YOU DOING IN THE WOODS OUTSIDE THE PRISON? PICKING BERRIES?

OF COURSE NOT, YOU--!

EXCUSE HIM, SIR. HE IS GIVEN TO FITS-- THE RESULT OF A CHILDHOOD ILLNESS.

BE GRATEFUL TO YOUR FRIEND, MAD ONE! OR WE WOULDN'T BE WAITING FOR THE ORDER TO KILL YOU!

LET ME GO, SPOCK. THERE'S GOT TO BE A WAY TO CONVINCE HIM--

THERE IS NO NEED, DOCTOR. HE KNOWS WE WERE NOT PRISONERS HERE.

THEN WHY HAVE THEY THROWN US IN THIS CELL?

TO GIVE THE APPEARANCE THAT FEWER PRISONERS ESCAPED--SO THEIR SUPERIORS WILL BE LESS APT TO PUNISH THEM.

4

AT LEAST THEY DIDN'T SEARCH US. YOUR COMMUNICATOR IS STILL A SECRET.

YES.

BUT THEY MAY CHANGE THEIR MINDS, ONCE THE SITUATION IS CALMER.

ONE CAN ONLY HOPE THAT CHIEF KYLE FINDS AN OPPORTUNITY TO BEAM US UP BEFORE A BODY-SEARCH BECOMES A POSSIBILITY.

SPOCK...THAT GUARD SAID SOMETHING ABOUT AN *ORDER* TO KILL US--DIDN'T HE? WHAT DO YOU SUPPOSE HE MEANT BY THAT?

YOU DID NOT ASK ME TO SET YOUR MIND AT EASE, DOCTOR McCOY. WHAT YOU ASKED FOR WAS AN APPRAISAL OF THE FACTS.

IT IS DIFFICULT TO SAY, DOCTOR. HE *COULD* HAVE BEEN BLUFFING--TRYING TO SCARE US.

OR HE COULD HAVE BEEN REFERRING TO AN *ACTUAL* ORDER.

"BLAST IT, SPOCK, YOU REALLY KNOW HOW TO PUT A MAN'S MIND AT EASE."

5

SO WE NEED YOUR HELP. AND WE NEED IT QUICKLY-- BEFORE THE AUTHORITIES CAN PUNISH MY FRIENDS FOR OUR ESCAPE.

WE ARE TIRED-- HUNTED. AND NOT ALL OF US MADE IT PAST THE GUARDS' NET.

WE WOULD LIKE TO HELP YOU, KIRK. YOU KNOW THAT, BUT OUR CAUSE REQUIRES PEOPLE TO KEEP IT GOING-- AND WHAT YOU ASK DEMANDS TOO BIG A RISK.

WHAT WE ASK WOULD BENEFIT YOU TOO, STROYKA. WE HAVE SHOWN THE AUTHORITIES-- AND THE PEOPLE--THAT THE POLICE CAN'T HOLD US. THAT THEY CAN'T STOP US!

THIS IS THEIR CHANCE TO PIN OUR EARS BACK. TO PROVE TO US THAT OUR VICTORY WAS A FLUKE.

BUT IT'S A CHANCE FOR YOU AS WELL. TO SHOW THE KRISAIAN REGIME THAT IT CAN'T IMPRISON ANYONE-- NEITHER YOU NOR ANYONE ELSE--WITHOUT JUST CAUSE.

6

YOU'VE TAKEN THE FIRST STEP-- BUT IT'S JUST THE *FIRST.* ARE YOU WILLING TO TAKE THE REST OF THEM?

IT'S *TRUE,* KIRK. NOW THAT WE'VE GOT A TOEHOLD, WE'VE GOT TO KEEP CLIMBING.

BUT WE'VE GOT TO PICK OUR STEPS *CAREFULLY.* WE'RE STILL JUST ONE SLIP AWAY FROM FALLING.

AND IN OUR PRESENT CONDITION, ANY FALL AT ALL COULD BE *FATAL* FOR US.

THEN YOU WON'T HELP US?

I CAN'T. I'M SORRY.

COME ON, CHEKOV. WE'RE NOT ACCOMPLISHING ANYTHING HERE.

7

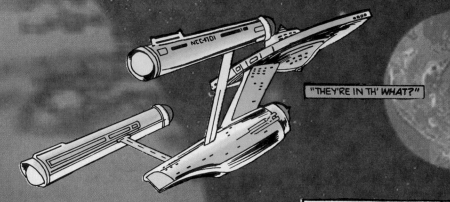

"THEY'RE IN TH' *WHAT?*"

IN THE *PRISON,* SIR. I'M STILL PICKING UP MISTER SPOCK'S COMMUNICATOR SIGNAL-- AND THE COORDINATES I'M READING ARE THE SAME ONES I HAD FOR THE CAPTAIN AND ENSIGN CHEKOV.

WELL, THEY COULD HAVE WOUND UP IN *BETTER* PLACES-- BUT AT LEAST WE KNOW WHERE THEY *ARE.*

ANY LUCK FINDIN' TH' CAPTAIN?

NOT YET, SIR. I'M AFRAID THAT'S GOING TO TAKE A WHILE. YOU KNOW HOW IT IS.

AYE, CHIEF. I'M AFRAID I DO.

WHAT T' DO *NOW?* I CANNA SEND DOWN *ANOTHER* RESCUE TEAM. THE PLACE IS CRAWLIN' WITH *ENTERPRISE* PERSONNEL ALREADY!

8

WE COULD JUST WAIT. BUT THINGS APPEAR T'BE GETTIN' WORSE, NAE BETTER.

I CANNA JUST SIT HERE ANYMORE. I NEED TO FEEL AS IF I'M *DOIN'* SOMETHING.

I'LL BE IN TH' TRANSPORTER ROOM IF I'M NEEDED.

I DON'T BLAME HIM. IT'S FRUSTRATING TO KNOW THAT GOOD PEOPLE MAY BE LOST-- WHEN WE HAVE THE RESOURCES TO GO DOWN AND GET THEM.

POOR SCOTTY. HE'S USED TO HAVING SOMETHING TO DO IN AN EMERGENCY.

IT'S FRUSTRATING, ALL RIGHT, LESLIE. BUT WHEN WE SIGNED UP, WE SAID WE'D PLAY BY THE RULES-- EVEN IF IT *KILLED* US.

REMEMBER BETA III? THE DANGER WE PUT OURSELVES? HELL, WE ALMOST *DIED* IN THAT RED HOUR IMPOSED BY LANDRU.

9

WHAT NOW?

NONE OF YOUR BUSINESS, REBEL! JUST GET A MOVE ON!

KRAK

CAREFUL WHAT YOU SAY, DOCTOR. WE DO NOT MEAN TO MAKE TROUBLE--DO WE?

WHY, OF ALL THE--

REMEMBER--WE DO NOT WISH TO DRAW ATTENTION TO OURSELVES.

I REMEMBER, SPOCK. IT'S JUST THAT I'VE GOT A BAD FEELING ABOUT THIS.

YOU ARE RIGHT TO HAVE A BAD FEELING, BROTHER. PRISONERS ARE TAKEN OUT FOR ONLY ONE REASON...

...TO BE EXECUTED!

12

LIEUTENANT?

MM?

COFFEE?

YES. THANK YOU, MEARS.

I DON'T ENVY YOU AT TIMES LIKE THESE, UHURA.

OH? WHY IS THAT?

WHEN THERE'S BAD NEWS, YOU'RE THE FIRST ONE TO KNOW ABOUT IT. AND YOU CAN'T REACT LIKE EVERYONE ELSE--YOU'VE GOT TO PASS IT ON.

ACTUALLY, YEOMAN, I THOUGHT ABOUT THAT BEFORE I WENT INTO COMMUNICATIONS. YOU KNOW, IN ANCIENT TIMES THEY USED TO *KILL* THE BEARER OF BAD NEWS.

"FORTUNATELY, THAT'S NO LONGER THE CASE."

AND *MOST* OF WHAT I HAVE TO REPORT IS *GOOD* NEWS. NEW PLANETS JOINING THE FEDERATION, NEW MEDICINES OBTAINED. DISASTERS AVERTED AND WARS ENDED AND PEOPLE'S LIVES MADE BETTER...

...THEN THERE ARE THE LITTLE THINGS-- THE PERSONAL THINGS. MESSAGES FROM FRIENDS AND LOVED ONES, BIRTH ANNOUNCEMENTS AND CONGRATULATIONS FROM SUPERIORS ON JOBS WELL DONE.

SO YOU TAKE THE BAD WITH THE GOOD--AND YOU DO THE BEST JOB YOU CAN.

YOU MAKE IT SOUND SO SIMPLE.

IT'S A SIMPLE JOB-- WHEN IT'S DONE RIGHT.

IT WOULD BE NICE IF YOU COULD REPORT SOMETHING GOOD-- AND SOON. THE CREW IS MORE THAN A LITTLE WORRIED ABOUT THE LANDING PARTIES.

I WISH I HAD A SAY IN THE MATTER, YEOMAN. ALL I CAN DO IS PRAY ALONG WITH EVERYONE ELSE.

BUT I CAN TELL YOU THIS--CAPTAIN KIRK HASN'T LET US DOWN YET. AND IF YOU ASK ME, HE WON'T LET US DOWN THIS TIME *EITHER*.

THEN THIS IS THE PLACE?

WITHOUT A DOUBT, KIRK. AND IT LOOKS AS IF WE'VE ARRIVED NONE TOO SOON.

I HAVE SEEN THIS BEFORE. IT IS AN *EXECUTION* PLATFORM.

"AND HERE COMES THE VEHICLE THAT CARRIES THE CONDEMNED. IF OUR INFORMATION IS ACCURATE, YOUR FRIENDS SHOULD BE ON IT."

"LOOK, KEPTIN! IT'S MISTER SPOCK--AND DOCTOR McCOY!"

CONGRATULATE YOUR SOURCES, STROYKA. THEY WERE RIGHT ON THE MONEY.

16

NOT THAT I'M TELLING YOU TO TAMPER WITH THE PRIME DIRECTIVE... BUT IF YOU HAD ANY *INTENTION* OF USING YOUR COMMUNICATOR, *NOW* WOULD BE THE TIME.

I INTEND FOR MY COMMUNICATOR TO BE DESTROYED WITH MY PERSON, DOCTOR. BUT I APPRECIATE THE SUGGESTION.

GREAT, SPOCK. IF YOU'RE PLEASED, I'M PLEASED.

I AM GLAD YOU DECIDED TO COME TODAY. THE PROCEEDINGS WILL BE HIGHLY *EDUCATIONAL*.

AFTER ALL, IT IS IMPORTANT TO KNOW WHAT SORT OF *PENALTIES* AWAIT THOSE WHO *DEFY* THE LAWS OF THE KRISAIANS.

EXECUTIONERS-- TAKE *AIM*!

IT'S BEEN NICE KNOWING YOU, SPOCK. WELL, MAYBE NOT *NICE* EXACTLY, BUT SORT OF *STIMULATING*.

I HAVE NOT BEEN ENTIRELY DISCOMMODED BY YOUR PRESENCE EITHER, DOCTOR.

18

KUH—

ROOOM!

THANK YOU, DOCTOR.

WE'VE GOT NO TIME FOR NICETIES, SPOCK. LET'S GET THE HELL OUT OF HERE!

UH-OH.

RUN--I WILL DEAL WITH THESE TWO AND CATCH UP WITH YOU.

DEAL WITH US, MISTER SPOCK? IS THAT A WAY TO TREAT YOUR COMMANDING OFFICER?

JIM!

IN THE FLESH, BONES-- AND I'D LIKE TO KEEP IT THAT WAY.

I HOPE YOU'VE GOT YOUR COMMUNICATOR, SPOCK.

AS A MATTER OF FACT, I DO.

"GOOD. THEN ALL WE NEED IS A SECLUDED SPOT."

"THAT MAY BE A RARE COMMODITY UNDER THE CIRCUMSTANCES, CAPTAIN."

OOMPH!

I'VE BEEN WANTING TO DO THAT!

HERE'S THAT RARE COMMODITY, SPOCK. LET'S TAKE ADVANTAGE OF OUR SOLITUDE.

SPOCK TO ENTERPRISE. FOUR TO BEAM UP.

ENERGIZE.

20

"CAPTAIN'S PERSONAL LOG, STARDATE 3012.7..."

"...IT'S GOOD TO BE BACK HOME."

ALAS!

THANKS FOR THE BOUT, LASALLE. I'LL SEE YOU LATER.

YOU ARE VERY GOOD VITH THAT SWORD. I VOULD LIKE TO LEARN HOW YOU DO THAT SOMEDAY.

I'LL BE GLAD TO TEACH YOU. THAT IS, IF YOU DON'T MIND A FEW *BRUISES* ALONG THE WAY--FENCING ISN'T AS GENTLE A SPORT AS IT'S MADE OUT TO BE.

I AM *USED* TO BUMPS AND BRUISES. LORD KNOWS, I RECEIVED MY *SHARE* OF THEM ON *MODALA.*

21

LISTEN, SULU... I VANT TO *APOLOGIZE* FOR THE VAY I TREATED YOU THE OTHER DAY. YOU VERE RIGHT--I *VAS* NAIRVOUS--BUT THAT VAS NO EXCUSE FOR BEING SO RUDE.

I WOULD LIKE TO START ALL OVER AGAIN MY NAME IS CHEKOV--PAVEL CHEKOV I'M NEW HERE. AND I COULD USE A *FRIEND*.

YOU KNOW, IT'S FUNNY. I KNEW SOME-ONE BY THAT SAME NAME. EXCEPT HE WAS A *GREEN APPLE*--SOMETHING YOU'RE OBVIOUSLY *NOT*.

FUNNY ABOUT THAT.

NOW...YOU *DID* SAY SOMETHING ABOUT LEARNING TO *FENCE*, DIDN'T YOU?

WHY DON'T YOU GRAB A MASK AND AN EPÉE AND WE'LL BEGIN.

ACTUALLY, I AM NOT *ENTIRELY* UNFAMILIAR VITH THIS SPORT. IT VAS INWENTED BY A *RUSSIAN*, YOU KNOW.

YOU DON'T SAY.

22

"DON'T BE TOO DISAPPOINTED, JIM. THEY CAN'T *ALL* BE WINNERS."

I HEAR YOU, BONES. BUT I HAD HIGH HOPES FOR MODALA.

TRUE--AND THEY'RE OFF TO A GOOD START. BUT IT COULD BE SOME TIME BEFORE MODALA IS READY TO BE CONSIDERED AGAIN FOR FEDERATION MEMBERSHIP.

IF THE REVOLUTIONARY MOVEMENT IS SUCCESSFUL, CAPTAIN, YOUR HOPES MAY YET BE *REALIZED*.

IN THE LONG RUN, THOUGH, I THINK THE TYRANTS *WILL BE OVERTHROWN*. THEY ALWAYS ARE.

I JUST WISH WE'D CLEARED UP THE MYSTERY OF THOSE WEAPONS BEFORE WE LEFT. WE MAY NEVER KNOW WHERE THEY CAME FROM-- OR WHY.

IN THE MEANTIME, ENSIGN CHEKOV ACQUITTED HIMSELF QUITE WELL, SPOCK. BETTER THAN YOU EXPECTED.

23

I THOUGHT YOU SAID IT WAS *LOGICAL* FOR INEXPERIENCED PERSONNEL TO GO ON AWAY MISSIONS!

IT IS.

YOU SAID THAT, SPOCK?

INDEED.

BUT BEFORE WE BEAMED DOWN--

I MERELY *RAISED THE QUESTION* OF MISTER CHEKOV'S INEXPERIENCE-- EXPRESSING NO OPINION ONE WAY OR THE OTHER. AFTER ALL, IT IS A FIRST OFFICER'S DUTY TO PRESENT ALTERNATIVES.

WHY DON'T YOU JUST ADMIT IT, SPOCK? YOU WERE AS UNCERTAIN ABOUT CHEKOV AS I WAS!

ON THE CONTRARY, DOCTOR. AS I TOLD YOU EARLIER--

YOU'RE NOT GETTING OFF THE HOOK ON A TECHNICALITY! NOT *THIS* TIME, YOU--

GENTLEMEN! CAN WE CONTINUE THIS CONVERSATION SOME *OTHER* TIME?

"TAKE US OUT OF HERE, MISTER SPINELLI. FULL IMPULSE."

"AYE, SIR. FULL IMPULSE."

"...HUNH...

"...HUNH...HUNH...

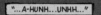

"...A-HUNH...UNHH..."

...HUNH...
HUNF...

...HUNH...
A-HUKK...
HUNHHH...

THIS STYLE SEEMED THE MOST PRACTICAL, SINCE IT OFFERS MAXIMUM PROTECTION AGAINST THE WATERY ENVIRONMENT.

WAS I IN ERROR?

I'M TRYING TO IMAGINE THE DOUBLE-TAKES AS HE WALKED DOWN THE CORRIDOR.

WELL, HERE'S WHAT THE *PROBLEM* IS, DATA.

THERE. MUCH BETTER.

ARE YOU CERTAIN, COMMANDER RIKER?

TRUST ME ON THIS.

IT ALSO HELPS IF YOU STAND LIKE THIS...

...PERFECT.

WHY IS THIS STANCE AN IMPROVEMENT?

IT DRIVES WOMEN WILD.

APPARENTLY YOU ARE CORRECT.

7

OWZ, HOW THE DEVIL DID YOU GET IN HERE?

ANGER OVER INJUSTICE LENT WINGS TO MY HEELS.

SPARE ME FROM PEOPLE WHO ESPOUSE PLATITUDES INSTEAD OF ATTITUDES.

STROYKA IS IN PRIVATE CONFERENCE NOW, OWZ.

STROYKA IS ALWAYS IN PRIVATE CONFERENCE, OWZ. HE HAS TIME FOR PRIVATE CONFERENCES WITH EVERYONE EXCEPT MYSELF AND MY FOLLOWERS.

PERHAPS HE JUST DOESN'T LIKE YOU.

PERHAPS YOU SHOULD DROP DEAD!

NOW THAT'S ENOUGH!

YOU HAVE GIVEN AN INORDINATE AMOUNT OF ATTENTION TO THE GOINGS-ON OF THIS CELEBRATION, STROYKA-- AND YOUR ATTENTION TO YOUR OWN PEOPLE IS SUFFERING FOR IT.

THE 100th ANNIVERSARY OF OUR LIBERATION-- A REVOLT WHICH LED TO OUR EVENTUALLY JOINING THE FEDERATION-- IS AN IMPORTANT OCCASION.

NONSENSE. THE ENTIRE THING IS AN ATTEMPT TO GRATIFY YOUR OWN MASSIVE EGO BECAUSE YOU WERE ONE OF THE REBELS INVOLVED-- HARD AS THAT IS TO BELIEVE.

YOU'VE PAID NO ATTENTION TO THE NEEDS OF YOUR PEOPLE FOR THE LAST YEAR! ALL AVAILABLE MONEY IS BEING DIVERTED TO THIS CELEBRATION, AND COULD BE BETTER USED FOR--

FOR IMPROVED SECURITY IN THIS OFFICE. UNTIL SUCH TIME AS I CAN AFFORD THAT IMPROVEMENT AND KEEP YOU OR YOUR FOLLOWERS OUT OF HERE...

...I'LL JUST HAVE TO ASK YOU TO LEAVE.

9

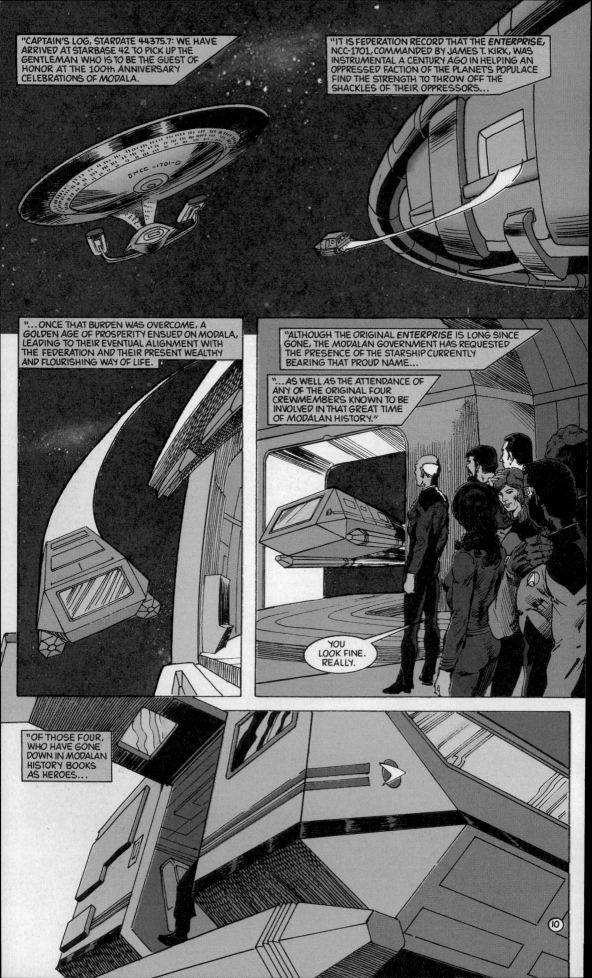

"CAPTAIN'S LOG, STARDATE 44375.7: WE HAVE ARRIVED AT STARBASE 42 TO PICK UP THE GENTLEMAN WHO IS TO BE THE GUEST OF HONOR AT THE 100th ANNIVERSARY CELEBRATIONS OF MODALA."

"IT IS FEDERATION RECORD THAT THE *ENTERPRISE*, NCC-1701, COMMANDED BY JAMES T. KIRK, WAS INSTRUMENTAL A CENTURY AGO IN HELPING AN OPPRESSED FACTION OF THE PLANET'S POPULACE FIND THE STRENGTH TO THROW OFF THE SHACKLES OF THEIR OPPRESSORS..."

"...ONCE THAT BURDEN WAS OVERCOME, A *GOLDEN AGE* OF PROSPERITY ENSUED ON MODALA, LEADING TO THEIR EVENTUAL ALIGNMENT WITH THE FEDERATION AND THEIR PRESENT WEALTHY AND FLOURISHING WAY OF LIFE."

"ALTHOUGH THE ORIGINAL *ENTERPRISE* IS LONG SINCE GONE, THE MODALAN GOVERNMENT HAS REQUESTED THE PRESENCE OF THE STARSHIP CURRENTLY BEARING THAT PROUD NAME..."

"...AS WELL AS THE ATTENDANCE OF ANY OF THE ORIGINAL FOUR CREWMEMBERS KNOWN TO BE INVOLVED IN THAT GREAT TIME OF MODALAN HISTORY."

YOU LOOK FINE. REALLY.

"OF THOSE FOUR, WHO HAVE GONE DOWN IN MODALAN HISTORY BOOKS AS HEROES..."

10

ADMIRAL, A PLEASURE TO SEE YOU AGAIN. WELCOME BACK ABOARD THE ENTERPRISE.

AND YOU ARE--?

CAPTAIN PICARD, SIR. WE MET WHEN YOU TOURED THE ENTERPRISE FOUR YEARS AGO.

OH. YES. OF COURSE.

YOU'LL FORGIVE MY OCCASIONAL LAPSE, CAPTAIN. THE ONLY ORGAN LEFT FROM THE ORIGINAL EQUIPMENT THE GOOD LORD GAVE ME IS MY BRAIN...

...AND IT GETS A LITTLE RUSTY EVERY NOW AND THEN.

THIS YOUR COMMAND CREW?

YES, SIR.

THE WHOLE THING?

YES, SIR.

THEN WHO'S RUNNING THE DAMNED SHIP? CADETS?!

OF COURSE NOT, SIR! WE HAVE A TRAINED--

IT'S A JOKE, SON.

PEOPLE SPENDING SO MUCH TIME GETTING THEIR ATOMS SCRAMBLED AROUND THE UNIVERSE, NO ONE HAS TIME FOR A DAMNED SENSE OF HUMOR ANYMORE.

12

COMMANDER WILLIAM T. RIKER, SIR. I AND SEVERAL OTHERS HERE JUST MISSED YOU LAST TIME.

WILLIAM T. RIKER. "T" STAND FOR TIBERIUS?

NO, SIR.

LIEUTENANT WORF. HEAD OF SECURITY.

USED TO BE A KLINGON ON THE SHIP MEANT A SECURITY ALERT.

THINGS CHANGE.

CHIEF ENGINEER GEORDI LAFORGE. AN HONOR, SIR.

THAT ONE OF THOSE VISORS THE MEDLABS DEVELOPED?

YES, SIR.

DEANNA TROI, SIR. SHIP'S COUNSELOR.

COULD'VE USED YOU IN MY DAY, GIRL. BET YOU COULD'VE WORKED WONDERS WITH A STUBBORN VULCAN I KNOW!

SPEAKING OF VULCANS, I DEFINITELY REMEMBER YOU!

YOU'RE THE ANDROID THAT TALKED LIKE A VULCAN.

I DO NOT DO SO CONSCIOUSLY, SIR.

OH? SAY "TOTALLY ILLOGICAL."

TOTALLY ILLOGICAL.

YOU'RE RIGHT! INFLECTION'S ALL WRONG. NEVER MIND THEN.

13

BEVERLY CRUSHER, SIR. I'M MEDICAL CH--

CRUSHER. OF COURSE. OF COURSE. YOU LOOK LIKE A FINE, HEALTHY WOMAN. GOOD TO SEE.

WHEN CREWMEN SEE THE MEDICAL PERSONNEL IN SUCH GOOD SHAPE, IT GIVES THEM CONFIDENCE THAT THEIR OWN HEALTH CARE IS IN GOOD HANDS.

WHY THANK YOU, ADMIRAL.

PHAW! ADMIRAL. THESE OTHERS CAN CALL ME BY USELESS RANKS, BUT NOT YOU. AT HEART, I'M JUST A PLAIN OLD COUNTRY DOCTOR.

I UNDERSTAND THERE HAVE BEEN IMPROVEMENTS ON THE SICKBAY SINCE I WAS LAST HERE.

YES, SIR, ADM... DOCTOR.

THEN BY ALL MEANS, LET'S GO CHECK THAT OUT, NURSE.

YES, SIR. ABSOLUTE--

--NURSE?!

14

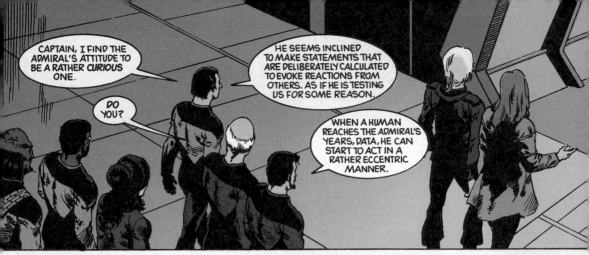

CAPTAIN, I FIND THE ADMIRAL'S ATTITUDE TO BE A RATHER *CURIOUS* ONE.

HE SEEMS INCLINED TO MAKE STATEMENTS THAT ARE DELIBERATELY CALCULATED TO EVOKE REACTIONS FROM OTHERS. AS IF HE IS TESTING US FOR SOME REASON.

DO YOU?

WHEN A HUMAN REACHES THE ADMIRAL'S YEARS, DATA, HE CAN START TO ACT IN A RATHER ECCENTRIC MANNER.

NOT AT *ALL*, NUMBER ONE. AT LEAST, NOT IN THE ADMIRAL'S CASE.

OH, AGE MAY HAVE *ADDED* TO HIS FORTHRIGHTNESS, BUT HE'S ALWAYS HAD A TENDENCY TO SAY *PRECISELY* WHAT'S ON HIS MIND.

WHEN I WAS IN THE ACADEMY, THE ADMIRAL WAS A GUEST LECTURER. HE SPOKE THAT DAY ON HOW THE INCREASED PERFECTION OF MACHINES THREATENED TO DOMINATE HUMANITY...

...TO THE POINT WHERE, IF WE WEREN'T CAREFUL, WE WOULD MAKE OUR OWN INSTINCTS AND INTUITION *SECONDARY* TO OUR INSTRUMENTATION.

IN THIS GREAT HUMAN ADVENTURE OF SPACE EXPLORATION, THE ADMIRAL WAS QUITE CONCERNED ABOUT THE LOSS OF THE *HUMAN* ASPECT.

HE WAS, IN FACT, ONE OF THE *FIRST* TO PUSH FOR THE INCLUSION OF FAMILIES IN DAY-TO-DAY STARSHIP LIFE.

STILL, CAPTAIN, AS DATA SAYS, HE DOES SEEM TO TRY TO *PROVOKE*--

WELL, THERE'S ONE OBVIOUS THEORY FOR THAT, NUMBER ONE.

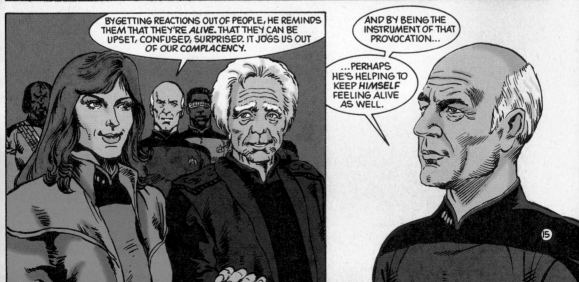

BY GETTING REACTIONS OUT OF PEOPLE, HE REMINDS THEM THAT THEY'RE *ALIVE*. THAT THEY CAN BE UPSET, CONFUSED, SURPRISED. IT JOGS US OUT OF OUR *COMPLACENCY*.

AND BY BEING THE INSTRUMENT OF THAT PROVOCATION...

...PERHAPS HE'S HELPING TO KEEP *HIMSELF* FEELING ALIVE AS WELL.

15

WE SHOULD BE ABLE TO *RENDEZVOUS* WITH THE *ENTERPRISE* IN APPROXIMATELY TWENTY HOURS, SIR.

THAT SHOULD PROVE SATISFACTORY.

SIR, IF YOU DON'T MIND MY ASKING... CERTAINLY SOMEONE OF YOUR RANK AND STATURE IS ENTITLED TO A CONVEYANCE OF MORE *IMPORTANCE* THAN THIS FREIGHTER.

I'M ALMOST EMBARRASSED THAT WE COULDN'T PROVIDE BETTER QUARTERS FOR YOU...

EMBARRASSMENT IS UNNECESSARY AND MISPLACED, CAPTAIN.

INTEREST IN FORM BEYOND FUNCTION IS A *NEEDLESS* INDULGENCE.

YOUR VESSEL WAS THE ONLY ONE IN THE SECTOR AT THE POINT WHEREIN MY SCHEDULE OPENED, PERMITTING THIS TRIP.

SINCE YOU SO KINDLY AGREED TO MAKE PROVISIONS FOR ME, IT WOULD BE MOST *INAPPROPRIATE* TO HARBOR SENTIMENTS OF INGRATITUDE. DO NOT CONCERN YOURSELF.

WHATEVER YOU SAY, SIR.

I SAY WE TAKE THEM NOW.

NO. REMEMBER THE PLAN.

WE WANT THE *ENTERPRISE* TO DROP OFF THEIR PASSENGER AND LANDING PARTY FIRST. THEY COULD MAKE MOST VALUABLE HOSTAGES.

WE COULD RUIN EVERYTHING IF WE ACT IMPULSIVELY. IF WE PROCEED CAREFULLY, ALL WILL OCCUR IN AN EQUITABLE AND FAIR MANNER.

16

18

WITH ALL DUE RESPECT, SIR, I THINK YOU'RE SELLING YOURSELVES SHORT.

OH, REALLY? SO TELL ME, BOY...

...ARE *YOU* A HERO?

WHAT? WELL... I DON'T THINK OF MYSELF AS SUCH...

COME ON, WILLIAM T-NOT-FOR-TIBERIUS RIKER. I'VE BEEN KEEPING UP ON YOUR ENCOUNTERS. NOT TO MENTION THAT BUSINESS WITH THE BORG. YOU'VE SURVIVED AND *TRIUMPHED* OVER *INCREDIBLE ODDS!* SO WHAT DOES THAT MAKE YOU?

DAMNED LUCKY.

DAMNED RIGHT!

AND I COULD USE A STIFF DRINK ABOUT NOW.

COMMANDER, THE *TEN FORWARD* WASN'T OPERATIONAL WHEN THE ADMIRAL WAS LAST HERE. WHY DON'T YOU ESCORT HIM? SPEND SOME TIME WITH HIM.

GLADLY, SIR.

"GLADLY"? YOU MUST BE A GLUTTON FOR *PUNISHMENT,* SON.

JUST EAGER TO LEARN, SIR.

SIR, WE ARE RECEIVING AN INCOMING HAIL FROM AN APPROACHING FREIGHTER SHIP. THE *TORNADO.*

ON SCREEN, LIEUTENANT.

20

ENTERPRISE, THIS IS LACEY OF THE TORNADO. WE HAVE A PASSENGER FOR YOU.

A PASSENGER? LACEY, THIS IS *MOST* IRREGULAR. WE ARE PRESENTLY EN ROUTE TO MODALA FOR A CENTENNIAL CELEBRATION.

WE CAN'T JUST START BRINGING ABOARD ADDITIONAL PASSENGERS. ESPECIALLY WHEN WE ARE TRANSPORTING SUCH IMPORTANT PERSONNEL AS ARE PRESENTLY ABOARD SHIP. THERE MUST BE *CLEARANCES* THROUGH STARFLEET...

IF I MAY...?

OH, BY ALL MEANS...

CAPTAIN PICARD. YOU ARE LOOKING WELL.

SIR! I HAD NO IDEA...

MY APOLOGIES TO YOU, SIR. HAD THERE BEEN TIME, I WOULD HAVE CONTACTED ALL THE PROPER AUTHORITIES.

AS IT IS, A LAST-MINUTE CHANGE IN MY SCHEDULE PERMITTED MY ATTENDANCE AT MODALA. IF, OF COURSE, IT IS PERMISSIBLE TO YOU...

BY ALL MEANS! MR. WORF, ARRANGE FOR OUR GUEST TO BE BROUGHT ABOARD AS SOON AS THEY ARE IN TRANSPORTER RANGE.

THANK YOU, CAPTAIN. I SHALL SEE YOU SHORTLY.

CAPTAIN... WAS THAT WHO I THOUGHT IT WAS?

ALL THAT YOU THOUGHT, COUNSELOR... AND *MORE*.

WELL, NOW, THIS IS CHARMING.

FIRST-HAND VIEW BEATS THE HELL OUT OF WATCHING THINGS OVER A VIEWSCREEN.

NOW, THIS IS *DEFINITELY* SOMETHING WE COULD HAVE USED IN *MY* DAY. A *BAR* ON THE *ENTERPRISE!*

IT'S NOT ACTUALLY A BAR, SIR. IT'S THE *TEN FORWARD LOUNGE.*

CAN YOU GET DRINKS HERE?

YES, SIR.

THEN IT'S A BAR.

ADMIRAL, THIS IS GUINAN. THE HOSTESS HERE AT THE BAR.

ACTUALLY, COMMANDER, I THINK OF TEN FORWARD AS A *LOUNGE.*

IF YOU CAN GET DRINKS, IT'S A *BAR.*

IT'S *NOT* A BAR!

SHE MAY BE RIGHT, BECAUSE THIS SURE ISN'T A DRINK. WHAT *IS* THIS?

SYNTHEHOL.

IT'S GOT THE KICK OF *SOAP SUDS!* YOU'VE GOT ENOUGH HAIR ON YOUR FACE, COMMANDER. NOW, WHERE'S A DRINK THAT'LL PUT HAIR ON YOUR *CHEST?*

GUINAN-- THINK YOU CAN FIND SOME KENTUCKY *BOURBON?*

HAH! I LIKE YOUR *STYLE,* COMMANDER.

22

HERE YOU GO, GENTLEMEN.

YOU SURE YOU CAN STILL *HANDLE* THE HARD STUFF, ADMIRAL?

WHAT DO YA THINK'S KEPT ME *GOING* ALL THESE YEARS, BOY? MY RADIANT *PERSONALITY?*

YOU KNOW, SON, YOU REMIND ME A LITTLE OF *JIM KIRK.*

I'M *HONORED,* SIR.

HOW ARE YOU WITH THE LADIES?

I GET MY *SHARE,* AND MAYBE A LITTLE MORE.

NOW YOU REMIND ME A *LOT* OF JIM KIRK.

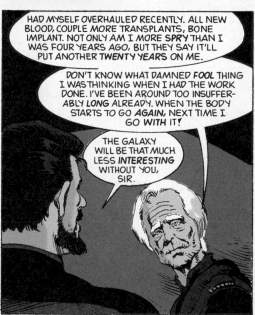

HAD MYSELF OVERHAULED RECENTLY. ALL NEW BLOOD, COUPLE MORE TRANSPLANTS, BONE IMPLANT. NOT ONLY AM I MORE *SPRY* THAN I WAS FOUR YEARS AGO, BUT THEY SAY IT'LL PUT ANOTHER *TWENTY YEARS* ON ME.

DON'T KNOW WHAT DAMNED *FOOL* THING I WAS THINKING WHEN I HAD THE WORK DONE. I'VE BEEN AROUND TOO INSUFFER-ABLY *LONG* ALREADY. WHEN THE BODY STARTS TO GO AGAIN, NEXT TIME I GO *WITH* IT!

THE GALAXY WILL BE THAT MUCH LESS *INTERESTING* WITHOUT YOU, SIR.

BUSHWA, SON. MY DAYS ARE PAST. ALL OF US. WE BELONG IN *HISTORY,* NOT IN STARSHIPS.

I BELIEVE, DOCTOR, THAT THE APPROPRIATE HUMAN VERNACULAR RESPONSE WOULD BE...

A *TOAST!* TO KIRK, SCOTTY, UHURA, SULU, CHEKOV, AND EVEN THAT DAMNED *VULCAN!* THE FINEST CREW THAT HISTORY EVER KNEW!

HEAR, HEAR!

23

"PERSONAL LOG, DR. LEONARD McCOY, STARDATE 44396.0: I HADN'T KNOWN HIM FOR FIVE MINUTES BEFORE HE STARTED TELLING ME HOW DAMNED SUPERIOR VULCANS WERE TO HUMANS.

"NATURALLY I TOOK THAT AS A CHALLENGE. SEEMED I SPENT THE REST OF MY LIFE TRYING TO *PROVOKE* HIM. SEE HOW MANY REACTIONS I COULD GET OUT OF HIM TO REMIND HIM OF HOW CLOSE HIS DESPISED HUMANITY LAY TO THE SURFACE.

"I WOULD'VE BEEN SATISFIED JUST TO SEE HIM *SMILE*. I NEVER DREAMED ALL THE WAYS THAT I WOULD SEE HIM OVER THE YEARS...

"...MURDEROUS...

"...ECSTATIC...

"...DYING...

"...REBORN.

"AND IT'S FUNNY. IN ALL THOSE DIFFERENT WAYS, AT ALL THOSE TIMES, I NEVER REALIZED THAT WHAT WAS MOST *IMPORTANT* TO ME...

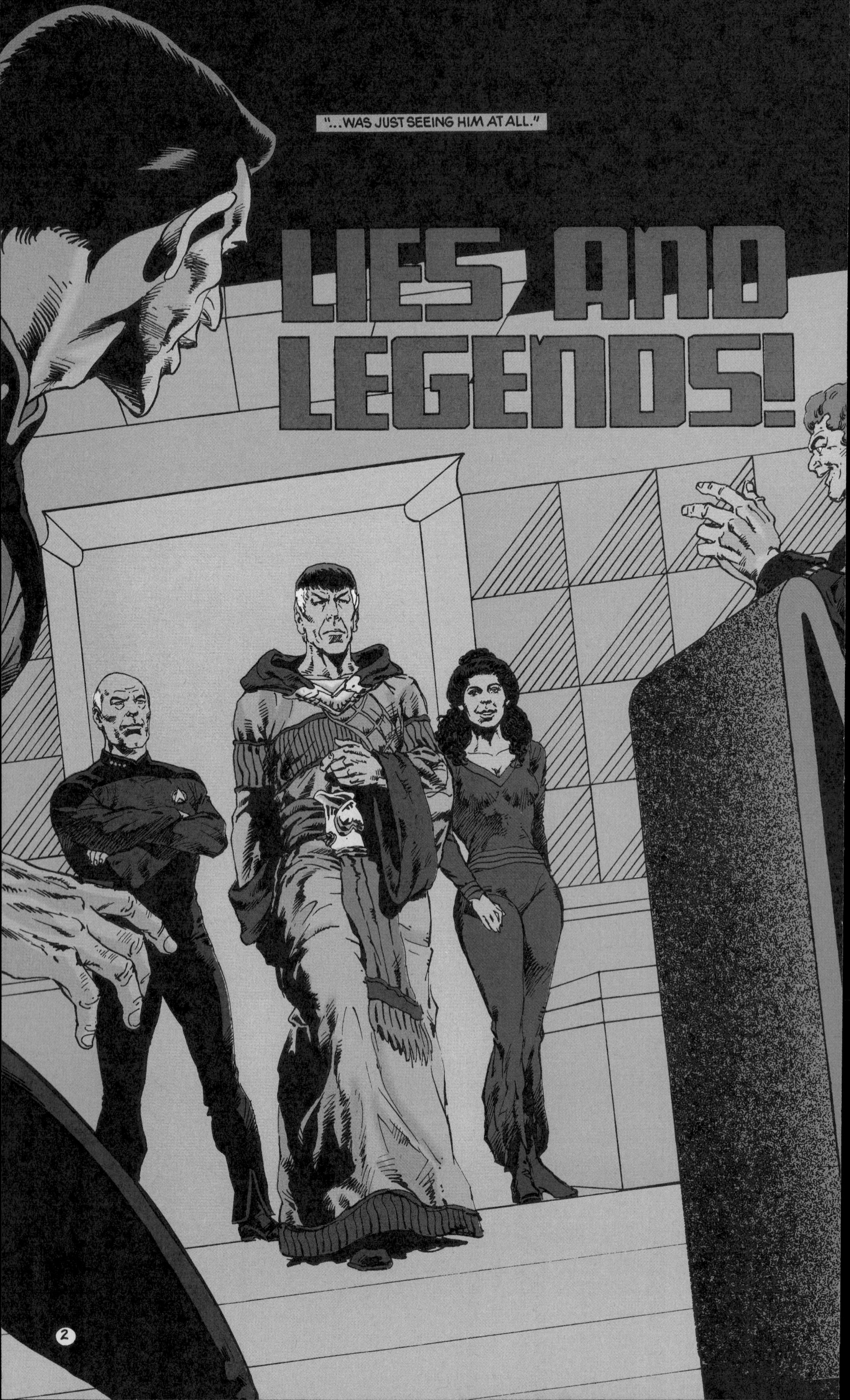

"...WAS JUST SEEING HIM AT ALL."

LIES AND LEGENDS!

PETER DAVID PABLO MARCOS
WRITER ARTIST

BOB PINAHA TOM McCRAW
LETTERER COLORIST

ROBERT GREENBERGER
EDITOR

BASED ON STAR TREK CREATED
BY GENE RODDENBERRY

3

SPOCK?

IS THAT...

...IS THAT...

...SPOCK?

CLEARLY, DOCTOR, THE YEARS HAVE NOT DULLED YOUR RAZOR-SHARP OBSERVATIONAL SKILLS.

SPOCK!

DAMN YOU, SPOCK!

YOU GOT *SOME* NERVE, JUST WALTZING IN HERE LIKE THIS!

COULD'VE GIVEN ME A *HEART ATTACK!*

INDEED, I HAVE OFTEN WARNED YOU, DOCTOR... THAT YOUR EMOTIONS WILL BE THE END OF YOU.

THEY PROVIDE...UNNECESSARY *BURDENS* ON THE CENTRAL NERVOUS AND CARDIOVASCULAR SYSTEMS.

DAMMIT, SPOCK... I'M A *DOCTOR.* NOT A *VULCAN!*

LEMME LOOK AT YOU.

YOU...

...WELL, FRANKLY, YOU LOOK LIKE HELL. I'D HEARD VULCANS LOOKED *BETTER* AT YOUR AGE!

INDEED. AND IT WAS *MY* UNDERSTANDING THAT HUMANS WERE GENERALLY *DEAD* AT YOUR AGE.

OOOH! HOW SHARPER THAN A SERPENT'S TOOTH IS THE WIT OF A *SENILE* VULCAN!

THEY DO NOT APPEAR *PLEASED* TO SEE ONE ANOTHER.

DON'T BELIEVE IT FOR A SECOND!

5

"CAPTAIN'S LOG, STARDATE 44396.2: WE HAVE SUCCESSFULLY RENDEZVOUSED WITH THE *ENTERPRISE*, DROPPING OFF AMBASSADOR SPOCK SO THAT HE CAN ACCOMPANY THE STARSHIP TO THE CENTENNIAL CELEBRATION ON MODALA.

"IN THE MEANTIME, WE ARE NOW EN ROUTE TO THE QAPMOC STAR SYSTEM, TO DELIVER OUR CARGO OF FOODSTUFFS TO..."

CAPTAIN LACEY. SENSORS ARE DETECTING ANOTHER VESSEL, APPROACHING AT WARP FOUR FROM A HEADING OF THREE-ONE-ONE MARK EIGHTEEN. INTERCEPT COURSE.

IDENTIFICATION?

NONE YET, SIR.

POWER TO DEFENSE SYSTEMS--

SHRAK SHRAAAK

6

7

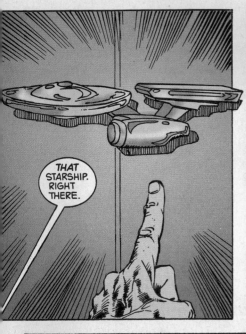

THAT STARSHIP. RIGHT THERE.

THAT'S THE *FIRST ENTERPRISE* THAT I SERVED ON. ME AND THIS VULCAN FELLOW RIGHT HERE.

AND WHICH ONE ARE WE ON?

THIS ONE RIGHT HERE.

OURS IS MUCH *BIGGER!*

IT CERTAINLY *IS,* BOY. BIGGER THAN WE WOULD'VE THOUGHT *POSSIBLE.* BIGGER *AND* FASTER.

WHY, YOU CAN CROSS SOLAR SYSTEMS IN SECONDS NOW. BUT IN THE DAYS OF MY ANCESTORS, IT TOOK *WEEKS* JUST TO CROSS NORTH AMERICA FROM ONE SIDE TO THE OTHER IN WAGON TRAINS!

WEEKS? WHY DIDN'T THEY GO IN AN AIR SHIP?

THEY DIDN'T HAVE 'EM! YOU WOULDN'T BELIEVE HOW QUICKLY THINGS CHANGE.

WHY, AS RECENTLY AS THE TIME OF MY *ENTERPRISE,* WE DIDN'T HAVE HOLODECKS. OR DILITHIUM CRYSTALS THAT COULD BE RE-ENERGIZED. OR LITTLE COMMUNICATORS ON OUR SHIRTS. *OR* FAMILIES ON SHIPS.

NO CHILDREN?

NOPE. NO CHILDREN.

8

IF THERE WERE NO CHILDREN ON SHIPS, AND GROWN-UPS FELT LIKE *PUNISHING* SOMEONE, WHO DID THEY PUNISH?

HIM.

THAT'S WHY WE STARTED HAVING VULCANS ON STARSHIPS. THEY DON'T *MIND* BEING PUNISHED.

I DON'T RECALL LEARNING ABOUT THAT IN THE ACADEMY.

IF YOUR SHIP WAS SO SMALL, WEREN'T YOU ALL REALLY *SQUISHED* IN THERE?

YEP! SO WE HAD TO WALK STOOPED OVER LIKE THIS ALL THE TIME!

HEE HA HA HEE HA

9

HEE HEE HA HA HA HA

IT WOULD APPEAR THE ADMIRAL IS PROVING QUITE ENTERTAINING TO THE CHILDREN.

THERE'S ALWAYS SOMETHING OF AN AFFINITY BETWEEN THE YOUNG AND THE OLD, DATA.

I WISH THEIR AFFINITY WERE BEING CARRIED ON SOMEWHERE ELSE!

INDEED, I MUST OBSERVE THAT THE PRESENCE OF SO MANY CHILDREN IN THE CONFERENCE LOUNGE IS, I BELIEVE, UNPRECEDENTED.

THE ADMIRAL REQUESTED IT, MR. DATA...WITH JUST ENOUGH OF AN EDGE TO MAKE IT A BIT MORE THAN A REQUEST.

UNDER THE CIRCUMSTANCES, I THINK THE CAPTAIN'S HANDLING IT WITH FAIRLY GOOD GRACE.

THERE, NOW, CHILDREN, YOU'VE HAD YOUR LOOK AROUND. LET'S ALL THANK THE ADMIRAL.

NOW GO ON BACK TO YOUR PARENTS. THAT'S GOOD CHILDREN.

THANK YOU, AD--

WELL DONE, CAPTAIN!

ESTIMATED TIME OF ARRIVAL AT MODALA?

AT PRESENT SPEED, NINE HOURS, EIGHTEEN MINUTES.

GOOD. THE MODALANS ARE DOUBTLESSLY ANXIOUS TO BEGIN THEIR CENTENNIAL CELEBRATION...

AND I AM UNQUESTIONABLY LOOKING FORWARD TO GETTING OUR GUESTS THERE.

⑩

PRETTY AMAZING, THIS READY ROOM, EH, SPOCK? IF JIM HAD SOMETHING LIKE THIS, HE'D'VE NEVER LEFT THE BRIDGE.

WHAT DO *YOU* THINK OF PICARD, SPOCK?

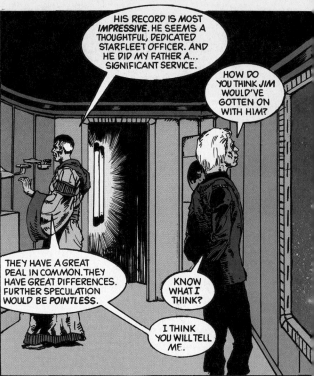

HIS RECORD IS MOST *IMPRESSIVE.* HE SEEMS A THOUGHTFUL, DEDICATED STARFLEET OFFICER. AND HE DID MY FATHER A... SIGNIFICANT SERVICE.

HOW DO YOU THINK *JIM* WOULD'VE GOTTEN ON WITH HIM?

THEY HAVE A GREAT DEAL IN COMMON. THEY HAVE GREAT DIFFERENCES. FURTHER SPECULATION WOULD BE *POINTLESS.*

KNOW WHAT *I* THINK?

I THINK YOU WILL TELL ME.

PICARD DOESN'T SEEM TO HAVE THE SAME INNER *DEMONS* THAT PUSHED JIM. NOR THAT SAME LOVE/HATE RELATIONSHIP THAT JIM HAD WITH THE *ENTERPRISE.*

JIM COULD NEVER HAVE ANY *OTHER* PERMANENT RELATIONSHIP BECAUSE THE *ENTERPRISE* WAS HIS *ALL-CONSUMING* LOVE.

NOW, PICARD...HE'S *PROUD* OF HIS COMMAND, THERE'S NO DOUBT. BUT IT DOESN'T SEEM TO HAVE BECOME THE BE-ALL AND END-ALL OF HIS EXISTENCE. IT'S PROBABLY A LOT *HEALTHIER.*

STILL, JIM WAS SOMETHING TO SEE IN *ACTION,* WASN'T HE? ALL PASSION AND PRIDE. HE AND PICARD WOULD PROBABLY *HATE* EACH OTHER.

IF YOU TRULY WISH TO EXAMINE IT, DOCTOR, THE QUESTION YOU SHOULD ASK IS...

...IF YOU WERE IN *DANGER,* WHO WOULD *YOU* WANT IN *COMMAND?*

TRUTHFULLY?

YOU.

AND IF YOU REPEAT THAT TO ANYONE... EVEN YOUR WIFE... I'LL DENY IT.

YOUR CONFIDENCE IS APPRECIATED. AND YOUR SECRET IS SAFE WITH ME...

...DOCTOR.

OH, HORSE MANURE! WE'RE JUST GETTING SOFT IN OUR OLD AGE, IS ALL.

WHY ELSE WOULD I SAY SOMETHING NICE ABOUT YOU? AND HOW COULD YOU PASS UP THE OPPORTUNITY TO TELL ME THAT I'M ONLY "BEING LOGICAL" WHEN I SAY I'D WANT YOU IN CHARGE?

THERE IS LITTLE POINT IN NOTING SOMETHING SO PAINFULLY OBVIOUS.

HMMPH.

OH, LOOK AT US, SPOCK. TWO TIRED OLD MEN. WE LOOK WORSE THAN WE DID WHEN THAT AGING DISEASE HIT US. REMEMBER? WHEN JIM WAS SO ADDLED HE COULDN'T EVEN RECALL THE NAME OF THE PLANET WAS GAMMA HYDRA THREE?

GAMMA HYDRA FOUR.

YOU EVER THINK ABOUT THE OLD DAYS, SPOCK?

THEY ARE RARELY FAR FROM MY THOUGHTS.

WHAT SINGLE THING DO YOU REMEMBER THE MOST? EDITH KEELER? THE THOLIANS? DYING? TIME TRAVEL?

WHAT ONE MOMENT DO YOU REMEMBER THE MOST CLEARLY? WHAT SINGLE INCIDENT HAUNTS YOU?

RECALLING HOW UNAESTHETIC THE CAPTAIN LOOKED WITH POINTED EARS AND ARCHED EYEBROWS.

SOMEHOW, SPOCK...THAT FIGURES!

"CAPTAIN'S LOG, SUPPLEMENTAL: A RATHER IMPROMPTU CONCERT HAS BEEN ARRANGED UPON THE DISCOVERY BY MR. SPOCK AND MR. DATA OF THEIR MUTUAL INTEREST..."

"...IN STRINGED INSTRUMENTS."

BRAVO! EXCELLENT! ENCORE!

WELL PLAYED, LIEUTENANT COMMANDER DATA.

THANK YOU, AMBASSADOR SPOCK. I CONSISTENTLY ENDEAVOR TO IMPROVE MYSELF.

YOUR VULCAN HARP SEEMS A MOST INTRIGUING INSTRUMENT. MAY I--?

YOU MAY ENDEAVOR TO PLAY IT, IF YOU WISH. HOWEVER, THE VULCAN LYRE IS A MOST COMPLEX INSTRUMENT. IT TAKES YEARS TO MASTER.

14

SOUNDS TO ME LIKE HE CAN PLAY AS WELL AS YOU CAN, SPOCK.

FASCINATING.

WHATEVER FACILITY I MAY HAVE ON THE VULCAN LYRE IS DUE ENTIRELY TO AMBASSADOR SPOCK.

NONSENSE, BOY. DON'T BE MODEST.

I COULD NOT BE, SIR. I AM MERELY STATING FACT. I WATCHED AMBASSADOR SPOCK'S MANIPULATING OF THE LYRE AND ACQUIRED THE KNOWLEDGE TO PLAY IN THAT MANNER.

AIN'T HE SOMETHIN', SPOCK? IMAGINE. A BEING BUILT BY A MAN THAT CAN OUT-VULCAN A VULCAN!

I FIND YOUR CHARACTERIZATION OF LIEUTENANT COMMANDER DATA SOMEWHAT SPECIOUS, DOCTOR.

OH, YEAH? I'D LOVE TO SEE YOU PLAY A GAME OF 3-D CHESS WITH HIM.

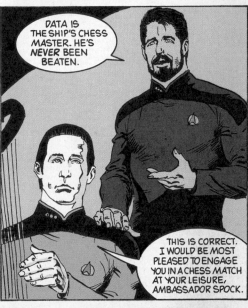

DATA IS THE SHIP'S CHESS MASTER. HE'S NEVER BEEN BEATEN.

THIS IS CORRECT. I WOULD BE MOST PLEASED TO ENGAGE YOU IN A CHESS MATCH AT YOUR LEISURE, AMBASSADOR SPOCK.

VERY WELL.

KNIGHT TO KING'S LEVEL TWO.

15

PLEASE! I'M SCARED! PLEASE!

JACKIE, THERE'S *NOTHING* TO BE SCARED OF.

AN APPENDECTOMY IS A ROUTINE OPERATION.

BUT I'M *REALLY, REALLY* SCARED!

WHAT COULD WE DO TO CALM YOU, JACKIE?

COULD YOU GET THAT NICE OLD DOCTOR TO COME AND BE HERE? COULD YOU?

DOCTOR McCOY?

YEAH! YEAH! *HIM!* JUST TO BE HERE.

I CAN GO GET HIM, BEVERLY, IF IT'S ALL RIGHT WITH YOU. THEY'RE JUST DOWN THE HALL.

NO PROBLEM HERE.

IN THAT CASE...

"...I'LL BE RIGHT BACK."

WHAT'S GOING ON IN HERE?

CHESS MATCH. ABOUT TWENTY MINUTES NOW.

BISHOP TAKES KNIGHT.

ROOK TO QUEEN'S LEVEL ONE.

WHERE'S THE *BOARD?* AND THE *PIECES?*

QUEEN TO KING'S LEVEL THREE.

IN THEIR HEADS.

BISHOP TAKES ROOK.

I SHOULD POINT OUT, SIR, THAT YOU WILL BE IN CHECK IN THIRTEEN MOVES.

INDEED.

AND YOU WILL BE IN CHECK...AND MATE...

...IN NINE.

16

INTERESTING. I HAD NOT ANTICIPATED THAT-- A VARIATION ON THE JAROCHA DEFENSE.

THE GAME IS YOURS, AMBASSADOR SPOCK.

AMAZING, GENTLEMEN. I'VE NEVER SEEN BETTER.

YOU ARE CLEARLY CONVERSANT IN EVERY KNOWN CHESS MOVE, MR. DATA. THE ONLY WAY TO DEFEAT YOU IS TO APPEAR TO FOLLOW ONE STRATEGY AND THEN DEVELOP A SIGNIFICANT DEVIATION.

YOU ARE CORRECT, SIR. HOWEVER, YOUR PARTICULAR VARIANCE WILL NOT WORK A SECOND TIME.

I HAVE NO DOUBT.

OF COURSE, COUNSELOR. I'D BE HAPPY TO.

SPOCK! PULL YOUR HEAD OUT OF THE CHESS CLOUDS. THERE'S A YOUNG LAD WHO NEEDS SOME MORAL SUPPORT.

COME ON, OR YOU AND SPOCK-IN-TRAINING WILL BE AT IT ALL DAY!

SO YOU'RE NERVOUS, BOY? HELL...AIN'T NOTHIN' TO BE NERVOUS ABOUT.

DR. CRUSHER, SHE'S AS GOOD AS THEY COME. AND AN APPENDECTOMY... HELL, SHE COULD DO THAT WITH HER EYES CLOSED!

IS SHE AS GOOD AS YOU?

HELL, BOY, OF COURSE NOT! BUT I'VE HAD EIGHT TIMES AS MUCH EXPERIENCE AS SHE HAS! NO ONE CAN DO THE JOB AS GOOD AS ME!

ALTHOUGH THERE HAS BEEN REMARKABLE PROGRESS WITH TRAINED BABOONS.

IGNORE HIM. HE'S SPENT OVER SEVENTY YEARS TRYING TO GET THE HANG OF HUMOR AND HE'S NO CLOSER THAN WHEN HE STARTED.

AMBASSADOR, I WAS HOPING THAT, AT SOME POINT, WE MIGHT DISCUSS VARIOUS ASPECTS OF VULCAN MENTAL DISCIPLINE. I BELIEVE IT WOULD HELP ME IN MY OWN DAY-TO-DAY WORK, AND ALSO BETTER PREPARE ME TO DEAL WITH SUCH DIFFICULT CASES AS YOUR FATHER.

AN EXCELLENT IDEA, COUNSELOR TROI. INDEED, IF I MAY SAY SO... I SENSE A CERTAIN DEGREE OF MENTAL AFFINITY FOR YOU. YOU SEEM A MOST DEFT EMPATH.

YOU ARE TOO KIND.

OH, AMBASSADOR SPOCK. THIS IS DOCTOR SELAR, OF MY STAFF.

NOT THAT SHE'D SAY SO, OF COURSE, BUT SHE'S QUITE ANXIOUS TO MEET YOU.

PEACE AND LONG LIFE, SIR.

LIVE LONG AND PROSPER, DOCTOR.

YOUR GRANDFATHER SERVED ABOARD THE INTREPID, IF I AM NOT MISTAKEN.

THAT IS CORRECT.

THEIRS WAS A TRAGIC LOSS.

THEIR MEMORY IS HONORED.

DOCTOR SELAR... YOU'RE VULCAN, LIKE AMBASSADOR SPOCK, AREN'T YOU?

YES.

DOCTOR McCOY SAYS VULCANS LIKE TO BE PUNISHED.

INDEED.

BRIDGE TO SICKBAY. AMBASSADOR SPOCK, ADMIRAL McCOY...WE WILL BE IN ORBIT AROUND MODALA IN TWENTY MINUTES.

THANK GOD.

18

"CAPTAIN'S LOG, SUPPLEMENTAL: WE ARE IN STANDARD ORBIT AROUND MODALA, AND AN AWAY TEAM CONSISTING OF MYSELF, COUNSELOR TROI, AND OUR GUESTS WILL BE BEAMING DOWN TO PARTICIPATE IN THE FESTIVITIES."

GENTLEMEN, AND LADY. I CANNOT TELL YOU HOW PLEASED I AM THAT YOU WERE ABLE TO ATTEND. IT IS A TREMENDOUS HONOR TO HAVE, NOT ONLY TWO OF THE INDIVIDUALS WHO WERE HERE AT THE TIME OF OUR REVOLUTION, BUT THE MAN WHO CARRIES ON THE PROUD TRADITION OF CAPTAINCY OF THE ENTERPRISE.

HARD TO BELIEVE YOU WERE INVOLVED IN THE REVOLUTION, STROYKA. YOU SURE DO AGE SLOWER THAN HUMANS. STILL, AT LEAST I HAD THE CHANCE TO AGE.

LAST TIME WE WERE HERE, WE BARELY ESCAPED BEING EXECUTED.

THOSE WERE AMONG THE FINAL, BRUTAL ACTS OF THE KRISAIAN REGIME--A REGIME OVERTHROWN THANKS TO YOUR CAPTAIN KIRK.

MY UNDERSTANDING IS THAT CAPTAIN KIRK... AND THEN-ENSIGN CHEKOV...MERELY BOLSTERED YOUR SPIRITS. THE DRIVE TO THROW OFF YOUR OPPRESSORS CAME FROM WITHIN YOU.

INDEED, STROYKA, YOU CANNOT DOWNPLAY YOUR OWN CONTRIBUTION TO YOUR PEOPLE'S LIBERATION.

WHATEVER. WE ARE HERE TO CELEBRATE THAT GREAT TURN-AROUND IN OUR LIVES. I SEE NO REASON TO DELAY THINGS. WE HAVE QUITE A CELEBRATION PLANNED...

...INCLUDING A RE-ENACTMENT OF OUR REVOLUTION...ALBEIT WITH SLIGHT EMBELLISHMENTS THAT THE RETELLINGS HAVE GIVEN IT.

"EMBELLISHMENTS"?

ONE CAN BUT IMAGINE.

19

ENTERPRISE TO CAPTAIN.

STROYKA, I WILL BE WITH YOU IN A MOMENT.

GO AHEAD, NUMBER ONE.

WE'VE JUST RECEIVED A DISTRESS CALL FROM THE TORNADO... THE FREIGHTER THAT DROPPED OFF AMBASSADOR SPOCK.

THEY WERE ATTACKED, BY PERSONS UNKNOWN. THEY'RE PRESENTLY CRIPPLED WITH NO PROPULSION AND LIMITED LIFE SUPPORT.

I SEE NO ALTERNATIVE, NUMBER ONE. BREAK OFF ORBIT AND GO IMMEDIATELY TO PROVIDE AID.

WILL YOU BE RETURNING TO THE SHIP?

NOT AT THIS TIME. IT SEEMS VERY IMPORTANT TO THE MODALANS THAT I AM HERE... AND THINGS SHOULD BE SAFE ENOUGH UNTIL YOU RETURN.

"AYE, SIR. WE'LL BE BACK AS SOON AS WE'VE SECURED THE SAFETY OF THE TORNADO. RIKER OUT."

IT WAS A *DARK* TIME FOR OUR PEOPLE.

THE KRISAIANS HAD RISEN UP AND PLACED THEIR OPPRESSION ON ALL FREE-THINKERS.

THEY CARRIED WEAPONS THAT SPIT DEVIL'S FIRE, AND WITH IT THEY LAID DOWN THE BODIES AND SPIRITS OF OUR PEOPLE.

OUR LEADERS WERE IMPRISONED...

...BEHIND THE GREAT WALLS OF THE KRISAIAN PRISON...

ALL WAS HOPELESS...

...WHEN SUDDENLY...

...THE GODS LOOKED DOWN UPON US, AND SAW THAT WE HAD WITHIN US THE ABILITY TO THROW OFF OUR OPPRESSORS...

...BUT WE NEEDED THE WILL AND THE WAY!

WHO DID WE NEED?

THE WILL! THE WAY! THE WILL! THE WAY!

22

YOU MUST BE *MAD* IF YOU THINK YOU CAN JUST WALTZ IN HERE AND LAY CLAIM TO OUR WORLD!

AND YOU ARE--?

STROYKA. THE RULING HEAD OF MODALA.

INDEED. THEN IT SEEMS WE'RE GOING TO HAVE YOUR RULING HEAD ON A PLATTER, AREN'T WE?

I AM NOT *MAD*. I AM EMINENTLY *SANE*.

THE ONE WHO HAS NO GRIP OF REALITY IS *YOU*, STROYKA! WE HAD A DEAL!

IT IS IN YOUR BEST INTEREST TO BE REASONABLE, DAIMON. YOUR "DEAL" WAS WITH A RULING CLASS OF A CENTURY AGO.

THEY ARE LONG GONE. OVERTHROWN. AND, FOR THAT MATTER...

...IF YOUR CLAIMS ARE TRUE, THEN YOU ARE IN VIOLATION OF FEDERATION *LAW* BY HAVING PROVIDED THE KRISAIANS, A HUNDRED YEARS AGO, WITH WEAPONRY TO HELP THEM OPPRESS THEIR FELLOW MODALANS.

ARRRHHHH!

NEHEMIAH!

FALL BACK! WE'RE PERFECT TARGETS UP HERE!

UNNHHH!

STOP... WAIT... WE CAN STILL...

I'VE CAUGHT THE *PRIZE!* DAIMON TRAN WILL BE *MOST* PLEASED.

UHHHHHHH...

YOU WILL HAVE TO SHARE YOUR ACCOMPLISHMENT WITH THE DAIMON AT A LATER DATE.

CAN YOU *WALK,* CAPTAIN?

I...I THINK...

YOU APPEAR TO HAVE SUFFERED A MILD CONCUSSION. YOUR REASONING FACULTIES ARE NOT CLEAN.

IT WOULD BE ILLOGICAL TO WAIT UNTIL SUCH TIME AS YOU ARE DEPENDABLY LUCID. NEVERTHELESS, I APOLOGIZE FOR THIS RATHER UNCEREMONIOUS TREATMENT.

BE AWARE THAT I STILL HAVE THE *HIGHEST REGARD* FOR YOU

GONE. MOST UNFORTUNATE.

THERE'S MORE *OVER* THERE! AFTER THEM!

STOP WHERE YOU ARE!

URKKH!

IF LIFE'S BEEN GOOD TO YOU, THEN COME WITH ME!

ONE CAN HARDLY RESIST SO GRACIOUS AN INVITATION.

"WHERE ARE THEY?!"

YOU HEARD ME! WHERE THE DEVIL ARE THEY?!

WE...WE DON'T KNOW, DAIMON. BUT WE WILL FIND THEM SHORTLY--

YOU'LL EXCUSE ME IF THAT ASSURANCE DOES NOT HOLD MUCH *WEIGHT* WITH ME!

THE WHOLE *PURPOSE* OF LURING THE *ENTERPRISE* AWAY WAS SO THAT WE COULD HAVE ITS OFFICERS AND EMISSARIES AS OUR *PRISONERS* WHEN WE TOOK OVER THIS PLANET!

YOUR INCOMPETENCE HAS INJURED OUR *BARGAINING* POSITIONS! HAVE YOU LEARNED *NOTHING* IN YOUR LIVES? IF YOU ARE NOT BARGAINING FROM STRENGTH, THEN YOU MIGHT AS WELL NOT BARGAIN *AT ALL!*

DAIMON, I...I DON'T *UNDERSTAND.* WHY DIDN'T WE JUST WAIT TO CLAIM THE PLANET UNTIL *AFTER* THE 100th ANNIVERSARY CELEBRATION?

BECAUSE MODALA IS A FEDERATION *MEMBER,* YOU IDIOT! WHENEVER WE LAID CLAIM, SOONER OR LATER THE FEDERATION WOULD HAVE SENT A STARSHIP TO *DEAL* WITH IT. AT LEAST *NOW* WE WOULD HAVE BEEN ABLE TO HAVE CONSIDER-ABLE HOSTAGES IN THE FORM OF STARFLEET PERSONNEL WHEN THAT DEALING IS DONE...

...BUT I DID NOT FACTOR IN YOUR *INCOMPETENCE.* I WANT PICARD!

BUT...BUT LOOK, DAIMON TRAN. WE DO HAVE *SOME* PRISONERS! SOME *VALUABLE* ONES.

BRING OUT THE PRISONERS!

13

PLEASE! BE *CAREFUL* WITH THE ADMIRAL. HE'S *FRAGILE*.

DON'T YOU WORRY ABOUT ME. I'LL GIVE THEM *FRAGILE* UP THEIR BODILY *ORIFICES*.

SEE? THE SHIP'S *COUNSELOR*. AND A HIGH-RANKING *ADMIRAL*.

AN *OLD MAN* AND A *WOMAN*. NO VULCAN AMBASSADOR. NO STARFLEET CAPTAIN. JUST AN OLD MAN AND A WOMAN.

YOU KNOW WHAT I SAY TO THAT?

NO, BUT I BET IT'LL BE SOMETHING *STUPID*.

QUIET, YOU!

YOUR LIFE IS HANGING BY A *THREAD*, OLD MAN.

NOT AS THIN AS THE THREAD *YOURS* WILL BE HANGING BY IF YOU HARM COUNSELOR TROI OR ME.

TROI? KIN OF *LWAXANA* TROI?

SHE IS MY *MOTHER*.

OH, THAT'S JUST *MARVELOUS!* YOU FOOLS!

DON'T YOU KEEP UP WITH GOSSIP? DON'T YOU KNOW THAT *ENTERPRISE* LOST ALL SENSE OF *DIPLOMACY* WHEN LWAXANA TROI WAS A CAPTIVE OF THE *FERENGI?* THE CAPTAIN'S *BESOTTED* WITH HER!

THEY WON'T BE WILLING TO *BARGAIN* OR *DEAL* IF WE HAVE THE DAUGHTER OF *LWAXANA!* IF THEY DO WHAT THEY DID LAST TIME, THEY'LL JUST BLOW US TO KINGDOM COME!

STOP THIS AT *ONCE!*

YOUR PEOPLE LOOK TO THE TWO OF YOU FOR *LEADERSHIP!* NOT PETTY SQUABBLING.

AMBASSADOR, HOW COULD YOU HAVE JUST *STOOD* THERE AND ALLOWED THIS... ALTERCATION... TO OCCUR?

I HAVE LEARNED THAT EMOTIONAL LIFE FORMS WILL ONLY BE SATISFIED WHEN ALLOWED TO EXPRESS THOSE EMOTIONS. HAD I INTERVENED BY, FOR EXAMPLE, RENDERING ALL COMBATANTS *UNCONSCIOUS...*

...THEY WOULD MERELY HAVE CONTINUED HOSTILITIES UPON AWAKENING-- AND FOCUSED THEIR ANGER ON ME FOR INTERFERING.

THIS WAY, THEY HAVE ONLY THEMSELVES TO BLAME FOR THEIR ILLOGICAL ACTIONS.

I WON'T DEBATE THE LOGIC OF THAT REASONING...

MOST WISE, CAPTAIN.

AND HOPEFULLY, STROYKA, YOU AND YOUR YOUNG CO-CONSPIRATOR HERE WILL BE ABLE TO PUT ASIDE YOUR DIFFERENCES AND COOPERATE IN DEALING WITH THE SITUATION.

WAIT. WHERE ARE THE ADMIRAL AND COUNSELOR TROI?

IN THE HANDS OF THOSE FANGED, BIG-EARED CRETINS ON TOP.

WHO THE HELL *ARE* THEY, PICARD?

17

REPRESENTATIVES OF THE FERENGI. A RACE MOTIVATED ENTIRELY BY PROFIT AND GREED.

THEY ALSO PROVIDE AN ANSWER TO A LONG STANDING "LOOSE END" IN YOUR WORLD'S HISTORY-- NAMELY WHERE DID THE KRISAIAN RULING CLASS ACQUIRE THE THEN-ADVANCED WEAPONS. THE FERENGI PROVIDED THEM...IN EXCHANGE FOR A PROMISSORY NOTE OF SORTS...

...THE COLLATERAL BEING THIS WORLD.

WE'RE NOT JUST GOING TO HAND OVER THIS WORLD TO THEM!

IT WOULD SEEM THEY DIDN'T ASK YOUR PERMISSION, STROYKA.

SPEAKING OF WHYS AND WHEREFORES... WHERE THE DEVIL ARE WE, ANYWAY?

AN ANCIENT SEWER SYSTEM. IT WAS BUILT NINETY YEARS AGO. USE WAS DISCONTINUED ABOUT TWENTY YEARS AGO WHEN NEW AND MORE EFFICIENT MEANS OF WASTE MANAGEMENT CAME INTO EXISTENCE.

ALL RIGHT, THAT ANSWERS THAT. NOW ANSWER THIS...

...WHERE ARE MY PEOPLE BEING HELD? I'VE GOT TO GET THEM OUT.

I REFUSE TO LEAVE THEM IN THE HANDS OF THE FERENGI A MOMENT LONGER THAN NECESSARY. WHAT THEY COULD DO TO THE ADMIRAL, YOU COULD NOT IMAGINE. AND WHAT THEY COULD DO TO COUNSELOR TROI...

...YOU WOULD NOT WANT TO IMAGINE.

18

I WOULDN'T BE TOO CONCERNED, COUNSELOR.

MAY I ASK, ADMIRAL, ON WHAT YOU BASE YOUR CONFIDENCE?

YOUR CAPTAIN AND MR. SPOCK ARE STILL RUNNING AROUND OUT THERE. LONG AS WE GOT THEM PLUGGING AWAY FOR US, SOONER OR LATER WE'LL BE OUT OF HERE.

Y'KNOW WHAT'S FUNNY, THOUGH?

NOTHING READILY.

A HUNDRED YEARS AGO, I CAME TO MODALA ON A RESCUE MISSION AND WOUND UP A PRISONER.

NOW I COME TO MODALA AN INVITED GUEST, AND WIND UP A PRISONER.

THERE'S A VALUABLE LESSON IN THAT.

THAT BEING--?

STAY THE HELL OFF MODALA!

I'D JUST AS SOON LEAVE NOW. I CANNOT SAY I LIKE THE WAY THAT GUARD IS LOOKING AT ME.

I'M SORRY YOU HAVE TO GO THROUGH THAT, MY DEAR.

I'LL BE SURE TO HAVE SPOCK PUT AN EXTRA NASTY NERVE PINCH ON HIM... JUST FOR YOU.

I SEE NOW. THESE SEWER SYSTEMS WERE PUT IN AT THE SAME TIME THAT THE JUSTICE BUILDING WAS BEING ERECTED ON THE SITE OF THE OLD JAIL BUILDING.

EXACTLY. NOBODY SNEEZE. THESE BLUEPRINTS ARE VERY OLD AND VERY BRITTLE.

WHEN THE JUSTICE BUILDING WAS CREATED, IT WAS FOR EXACTLY THAT PURPOSE. IT'S WHERE TRIALS ARE HELD, JUDGMENTS MADE. AS OPPOSED TO THE PRISON BUILDING THAT WAS THERE WHERE MODALANS WERE SIMPLY DEPOSITED, WITHOUT TRIAL, TO ROT...

...HOWEVER, THERE ARE HOLDING CELLS IN THE SUBLEVELS OF THE JUSTICE BUILDING. TAKING A GUESS, I'D SAY THAT'S WHERE YOUR PEOPLE ARE.

LOOK HERE. IF I'M READING THIS CORRECTLY, THE SEWER SYSTEM IS SEPARATED AT THAT POINT THERE FROM THE SUBLEVELS BY ONLY A COUPLE YARDS OF WALL.

THAT'S RIGHT. AT THE TIME, THESE SEWERS WERE FILLED WITH WATER. YOU'D NEED WEAPONS TO BREAK OUT FROM THE JAIL THROUGH THE WALL, WHICH NATURALLY PRISONERS DIDN'T HAVE...

...AND ALL THE WATER IN THE SEWERS MADE IT IMPOSSIBLE FOR SOMEONE TO BREAK IN. BY THE TIME THE RENOVATIONS WERE DONE, PEOPLE HAD GENERALLY FORGOTTEN ABOUT THE PROXIMITY. NO ONE'S CHECKED OUT THESE BLUE-PRINTS IN YEARS...

I DID. I, AND MY PEOPLE.

WELL...NO ONE OF IMPORTANCE.

OWZ...CAN YOU GET YOUR HANDS ON SOME WEAPONS?

OF COURSE.

GOOD. THEN HERE'S WHAT WE DO...

20

SO THEY GAVE YOU NO WARNING?

NCC 1701-D

NONE, COMMANDER. WE WERE MINDING OUR OWN BUSINESS AND, FOR NO REASON WHATSOEVER, THEY ATTACKED US...

AND THEN, WHEN THEY HAD US AT THEIR MERCY... THEY SIMPLY LEFT.

I HAVE TAKEN THE LIBERTY OF TRANSFERRING THE SHIPS LOGS OF THE *TORNADO* TO THE *ENTERPRISE* COMPUTER. WE CAN ACCESS THE VISUAL RECORD OF THE ATTACK ON THE *TORNADO*.

DO IT, MR. DATA.

THAT'S THEM, ALL RIGHT.

YOU KNOW... NOW THAT I HAVE A CHANCE TO STUDY IT... THAT LOOKS LIKE--

FERENGI.

ABSOLUTELY.

NO QUESTION.

MR. DATA, HOW LONG UNTIL WE FINISH LOADING THE CARGO AND CREW OF THE TORNADO ONTO THE *ENTERPRISE*?

ESTIMATED TIME OF TRANSFER COMPLETION: FORTY-THREE MINUTES.

AS SOON AS WE'RE DONE, BEST SPEED TO MODALA.

21

BUT COMMANDER, OUR CARGO...IT HAS TO BE DELIVERED TO QAPMOC...

THE PEOPLE OF QAPMOC WILL HAVE TO WAIT, CAPTAIN LACEY. FOR THAT MATTER, SO WILL YOUR SHIP. I DON'T WANT TO SLOW US DOWN BY TAKING IT IN TOW.

I THINK YOU SHOULD KNOW I'LL REGISTER A FORMAL COMPLAINT WITH STARFLEET OVER THIS.

AND I THINK *YOU* SHOULD KNOW, CAPTAIN, THAT I DON'T GIVE A DAMN WHAT YOU DO. I HAVE A FEELING THAT THE PURPOSE OF THE ATTACK ON YOU WAS TO LURE US AWAY FROM MODALA.

IF THAT'S THE CASE, THERE IS POTENTIAL DANGER TO THE AWAY TEAM. AND I AM NOT GOING TO HAUL CARGO WHEN I THINK THERE'S AN AWAY TEAM IN TROUBLE. YOU'RE LUCKY I'M TAKING THE TIME TO LOAD IT AT ALL.

I CAN'T SAY I APPROVE OF YOUR PRIORITIES, COMMANDER. MILLIONS OF PEOPLE ARE DEPENDING ON THAT CARGO.

SINCE IT'S THAT *IMPORTANT* TO YOU, CAPTAIN LACEY...

...WE'LL HITCH THE CARGO UP TO A HARNESS AND YOU CAN HAUL IT TO QAPMOC...

...ON FOOT!

IF THAT'S YOUR PLEASURE, YOU CAN START WALKING. UNTIL THEN...PLEASE LEAVE THE BRIDGE.

NOW.

MR. DATA, WORK WITH SHIP'S SERVICES AND GET THAT CARGO LOADED FASTER. I WANT TO BE OUT OF HERE IN HALF AN HOUR, TOPS.

AND LET GEORDI KNOW WE'LL BE WANTING WARP *NINE.*

YES, SIR.

YOU'RE POSITIVE THIS IS THE JUNCTURE?

ABSOLUTELY. ALL WE HAVE TO DO IS PUNCH THROUGH AND WE'LL BE IN THE LOWER LEVELS OF THE JUSTICE BUILDING.

ONLY PROBLEM IS, WE'LL BE MAKING THE DEVIL'S OWN NOISE WHEN WE BLAST THROUGH. IF THE FERENGI HAVE ANY GUARDS AT ALL WATCHING THE PRISONERS, THEY'LL BE ALERTED.

WHICH MEANS WE HAVE TO COUNT ON OWZ AND HIS PEOPLE TO CREATE THE DISTRACTION TOPSIDE.

PERHAPS IT WOULD HAVE BEEN WISER IF I HAD ACCOMPANIED HIM...

YOU'RE TOO IMPORTANT TO THE FEDERATION, AMBASSADOR, FOR ME TO HAVE YOU RUNNING ABOUT...PARTICULARLY AS A SITTING DUCK.

RUNNING AND SITTING ARE MUTUALLY EXCLUSIVE.

I'LL TRY TO WATCH THAT.

TIME CHECK?

OWZ AND HIS PEOPLE SHOULD HAVE BEGUN THEIR ASSAULT... PRECISELY TWO MINUTES AGO.

WHICH MEANS, THEORETICALLY, THAT THE FERENGI WILL BE DEPLOYING ALL AVAILABLE FORCES TO STOP THEM, BELIEVING IT TO BE A JAILBREAK ATTEMPT...

NOT REALIZING THE TRUE ASSAULT IS FROM BELOW.

...THAT IS THE THEORY. WEAPONS READY AND...

...FIRE!

SHREEEE

23

SHRAKOOM

WE DID IT! WE'RE THROUGH.

THIS IS ALL PROGRESSING RATHER SMOOTHLY.

YES. PERHAPS EVEN *TOO* SMOOTHLY.

AH. CAPTAIN. AMBASSADOR. STROYKA AND COMPANIONS...

...DAIMON TRAN. OR PERHAPS YOU REMEMBER. NOW THEN...

...PLEASE PUT DOWN YOUR WEAPONS...OR THINGS ARE GOING TO GET A TRIFLE...

...BLOODY.

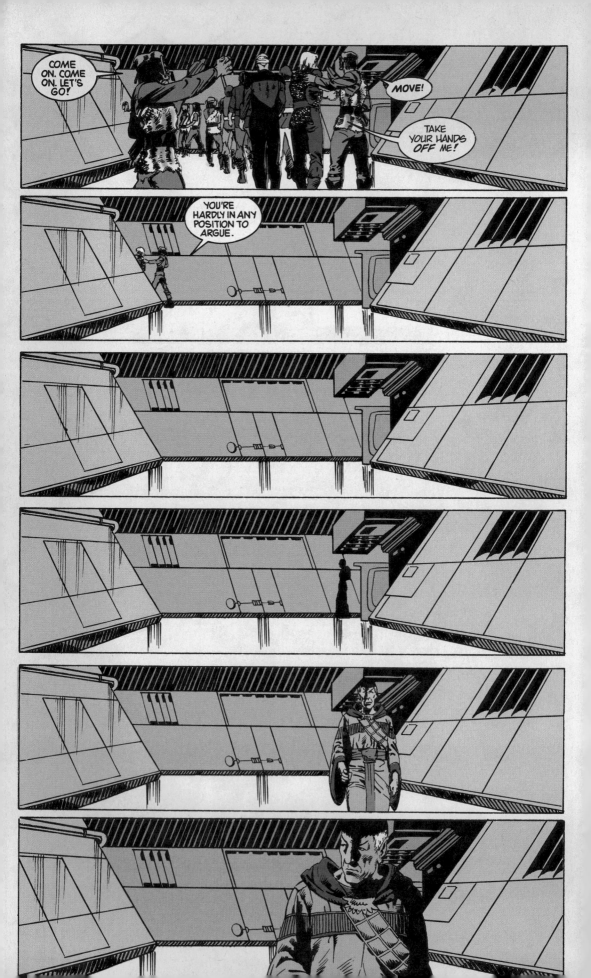

DAIMON... MAY I ASK SOMETHING...?

OF COURSE, KRAG.

YOU HAD SAID THAT WHEN IT CAME TIME TO STRIP THE FEMALE, THAT I WOULD HAVE THE *HONOR*. WELL...SINCE SHE HAS SERVED HER PURPOSE AS *BAIT*, AND WE HAVE NO OTHER PARTICULAR USE FOR HER THAT WOULD REQUIRE HER TO BE *CLOTHED*...?

I THINK YOU MIGHT BE RIGHT AT THAT, KRAG. ENJOY YOURSELF.

YOU ARE *NOT* TO TOUCH COUNSELOR TROI! THAT IS A DIRECT *ORDER*!

THIS IS NOT YOUR PATHETIC *BRIDGE*, AND YOUR AUTHORITY IS LIMITED TO WHAT WE *SAY* IT IS! YOU CAN'T ORDER *ME*!

OH, HE CAN *ORDER* YOU ALL HE WISHES, KRAG. BUT YOU'RE HARDLY OBLIGED TO *OBEY*. BE OFF WITH YOU! I'LL ATTEND TO THE CAPTAIN HERE.

WELL, PICARD. YOU'RE EVERYTHING I'D HEARD YOU WERE.

THANK YOU.

IT WAS NOT INTENDED AS A *COMPLIMENT*.

7

I'D HEARD YOU WERE SMUG, EGOTISTICAL, IMPERIOUS...

...AND OVERWHELMED BY A SENSE OF YOUR OWN IMPORTANCE.

WHAT DO YOU SAY TO THAT?

I SAY THAT THAT IS THE OPINION OF THE FERENGI. AND IN SUCH INSTANCES...

...I TEND TO CONSIDER THE SOURCE.

OH, VERY GOOD, PICARD. VERY GOOD. "CONSIDER THE SOURCE." I LIKE THAT.

AND WHAT WOULD YOU SAY IF THIS "SOURCE" INFORMED YOU THAT WE WERE GOING TO DRAG YOU OUT TO THAT SQUARE, RIGHT OUTSIDE...

...AND SHOOT YOU DEAD...?

I WOULD SAY THAT THAT IS TYPICAL FERENGI FOOLISHNESS. THAT IT'S A BLUFF.

THAT A STARFLEET CAPTAIN IS A VALUABLE DEALING COMMODITY, AND A FERENGI WOULDN'T TOSS AWAY SUCH A USEFUL CARD UNTIL HE'S HAD TIME TO PLAY IT. ESPECIALLY SINCE YOU MUST KNOW...

...THAT THE ENTERPRISE IS CERTAINLY ON HER WAY BACK FROM WHATEVER LITTLE GOOSE CHASE YOU ARRANGED TO SEND HER ON! A DEAD COMMANDER WILL LEAVE YOU NOTHING WITH WHICH TO BARGAIN.

AND YOU REGARD SUCH A BARGAINING STRATEGY AS THE CORRECT ONE?

NO. BECAUSE I AM JUST ONE CREWMAN. MY SHIP WOULD SOONER DESTROY THE ENTIRE PLANET, WITH MYSELF INCLUDED, THAN BARGAIN WITH TREACHEROUS BACKSTABBERS SUCH AS YOURSELF.

AH, PICARD, YOU DO NOT HOLD A POKER FACE NEARLY AS WELL AS A FERENGI. WE BOTH KNOW THAT YOUR SHIP WILL DO WHATEVER IT TAKES TO ASSURE THE SAFETY OF YOU, THE VULCAN, AND--

--THE VULCAN! WAIT A MINUTE! WHERE IS HE?

HE WAS WITH THEM WHEN...

...WHERE IS HE?!

8

SO...

...THEY MAKING THE VULCAN NECK PINCH A REQUIRED TECHNIQUE AT THE ACADEMY THESE DAYS?

AS ALWAYS, DOCTOR, YOUR ANALYSIS OF THE SITUATION FAILS TO GRASP THE OBVIOUS.

KINDLY RELIEVE THE GUARD OF HIS KEYS SO THAT WE MAY PROCEED, WITH ALL DUE ALACRITY, TO A PLACE OF MARGINALLY GREATER SAFETY.

13

AND WHAT ABOUT YOU, OWZ? WON'T YOU TAKE THIS OPPORTUNITY TO LIVE?

DEATH IS FAR PREFERABLE TO A LIFE OF SERVITUDE TO THESE FANGED, STOOPED, HAIRLESS CRETINS, WITH THEIR BAD MANNERS AND BAD BREATH.

I MAY HAVE BEEN A LESS THAN STELLAR COMMANDER, BUT I'LL BE DAMNED IF I BECOME GUTLESS. MY ONLY REGRET IS THAT MORE OF MY OWN FOLLOWERS APPARENTLY DON'T SHARE MY SENTIMENTS. SEE THEM THERE, QUAVERING NEXT TO YOURS?

YOU WOULD SEEM TO HAVE SOME OF THE SAME WEAKNESSES... NOT TO MENTION SOME OF THE SAME DAMNED STUBBORNNESS. THE SORT OF PRIDE IN YOURSELVES AND IN YOUR PLANET THAT BEFITS LEADERS.

PEACEMAKER TO THE END, NEERA? AND PERHAPS... YOU HAVE A POINT THERE.

PERHAPS SHE DOES AT THAT. I ALWAYS WAS OF THE OPINION THAT YOUR MATE WAS THE TRUE BRAINS OF GOVERNMENT.

I WOULD TEND TO AGREE.

I ONLY REGRET THAT NOW, WHEN IT MATTERS MOST, HER FAMED WITS SEEM TO HAVE DESERTED HER AND SHE DOESN'T KNOW WHAT'S BEST FOR HER.

SAVE YOURSELF, NEERA. GO WITH THEM.

AND BE THE SAME AS THOSE YOU DESPISE? NO THANK YOU.

I WOULD NOT THINK THE LESS OF YOU.

YOU LIE. BESIDES, YOU WOULDN'T BE THINKING AT ALL. YOU'D BE DEAD. AND I WOULD BE LEFT THINKING THOUGHTS I'D RATHER NOT THINK, THANK YOU.

WHATEVER HAPPENS... HAPPENS.

VERY WELL THEN. FIRING SQUAD, PREPARE TO--

WAIT!

OH, WHAT NOW, PICARD?

LET'S... DEAL.

16

HOW DO YOU **DO** THAT? JUST NOT BE NOTICED THAT WAY?

I BELIEVE THE HUMAN TERM FOR IT WOULD BE...

...A "KNACK."

NOW LET'S SEE IF I UNDERSTAND THIS. YOU WISH TO CHALLENGE ME TO PERSONAL COMBAT, WITH THE LIVES OF THESE MODALANS AND THE PLANET'S FREEDOM AS THE STAKES. AND YOU ARE PUTTING UP AGAINST THOSE STAKES...THE **ENTERPRISE?**

THAT'S **ABSURD.** YOU DON'T HAVE THAT AUTHORITY.

OF **COURSE** I DO. I AM A REPRESENTATIVE OF THE FEDERATION. IT WOULD BE THE EQUIVALENT OF SURRENDERING MY SHIP... CERTAINLY WELL WITHIN MY PURVIEW AS **ENTERPRISE COMMANDER,** AND SOMETHING I HAVE BEEN WILLING TO DO BEFORE WHEN INNOCENT LIVES ARE AT STAKE. DO WE HAVE A **DEAL?**

I'M NOT SURE IF I BELIEVE YOU OR NOT...

I'LL GIVE YOU, IN WRITING, THE AUTHORITY TO TAKE COMMAND OF THE **ENTERPRISE** SHOULD I LOSE. MY WORD AND REPUTATION ARE **SPOTLESS.**

BELIEVING ME IS NOT THE DIFFICULTY...

...DEFEATING ME IS!

UNLESS, OF COURSE... YOU THINK YOU **CAN'T.**

17

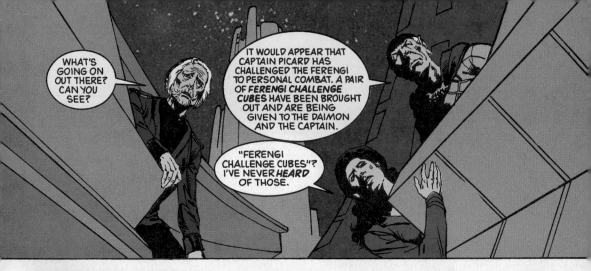

WHAT'S GOING ON OUT THERE? CAN YOU SEE?

IT WOULD APPEAR THAT CAPTAIN PICARD HAS CHALLENGED THE FERENGI TO PERSONAL COMBAT. A PAIR OF *FERENGI CHALLENGE CUBES* HAVE BEEN BROUGHT OUT AND ARE BEING GIVEN TO THE DAIMON AND THE CAPTAIN.

"FERENGI CHALLENGE CUBES"? I'VE NEVER *HEARD* OF THOSE.

"FERENGI CHALLENGE CUBES, COUNSELOR, ARE SEMI-SENTIENT PSYCHIC ASSAULT CUBES WHICH... PUT SIMPLY... DO NOT LIKE TO BE *TOUCHED.*"

"THE CHALLENGE IS THAT ONE IS SUPPOSED TO MAINTAIN A FIRM GRIP ON A CUBE WHILE THE RATHER BELLIGERENT LIFE FORM MENTALLY ASSAULTS THE HOLDER IN AN ENDEAVOR TO BE RELEASED."

"THE WINNER IS WHOEVER HAS MANAGED TO RETAIN HIS MENTAL FACULTIES AGAINST THE CUBE'S BARRAGE. WHOEVER DROPS THEIR RESPECTIVE CUBE FIRST LOSES."

I WARN YOU, CAPTAIN. I HAVE ENGAGED IN THIS CHALLENGE MANY A TIME... AND *NEVER LOST.* LAST CHANCE TO BACK OUT.

BEGIN.

AARRUNH!

COUNSELOR!

HELP HIM! THE--

--THE IMAGES--

--GODS, IT'S--

--HELP HIM!

"HELP HIM! PLEASE! DO SOMETHING! IT'S DESTROYING HIM!"

19

I'LL BE DAMNED. I THINK I JUST FOUND HOW THE DAIMON BECAME SUCH A CHAMP ON THESE CUBE THINGS.

SOME SORT OF IMPLANT. SHORED HIM UP MENTALLY TO WITHSTAND THE CUBES, LONG ENOUGH TO OUTLAST ANY OTHER COMPETITOR...UNTIL NOW.

THAT SOUND--!

TRANSPORTERS! NEVER THOUGHT I'D BE SO GLAD TO HEAR THOSE THINGS!

CAPTAIN! ARE YOU ALL RIGHT?

TRUTHFULLY, NUMBER ONE, I HAVE HAD BETTER DAYS.

THERE'S A FERENGI SHIP IN ORBIT...BUT, WITH NO EXPLANATION, THEY JUST POWERED DOWN THEIR WEAPONS...

THE EXPLANATION IS THAT THEY NO LONGER HAVE ANY CLAIM HERE.

THIS IS MOST UNFAIR! THE WEAPONS THAT WE GAVE THESE PEOPLE IN OUR ORIGINAL DEAL--

YOU WANT THEM BACK? TAKE THEM BACK! I UNDERSTAND THEY'RE PRESENTLY IN A MODALAN MUSEUM.

OF COURSE THEY ARE! THEY'RE A CENTURY OLD! THEY'RE ANTIQUES! WE DIDN'T WANT THEM, WE WANTED THE PLANET...

YOU NO LONGER HAVE ANY CLAIM. AND IF YOU STILL WISH TO HAVE A SHIP...I SUGGEST YOU LEAVE. NOW.

UNLESS, OF COURSE, YOU'D RATHER...

NO! NO, THAT'S QUITE ALL RIGHT. WE WERE...

....JUST LEAVING.

23

"CAPTAIN'S LOG, STARDATE 44398.7: WE HAVE STAYED LONG ENOUGH TO ENSURE THE DEPARTURE OF THE FERENGI... AND, IN AN INTERESTING SIDELINE, WITNESS THE APPOINTMENT BY STROYKA OF A NEW SECOND-IN-COMMAND: OWZ.

"I SUSPECT THERE WILL BE A GREAT DEAL THAT THEY CAN LEARN FROM ONE ANOTHER. IT IS REGRETTABLE THAT THE ANNIVERSARY CELEBRATION ON MODALA WAS DISRUPTED, AND YET... STROYKA IS NOW OF THE OPINION THAT IT MAY HAVE BEEN THE BEST THING THAT COULD HAVE HAPPENED FOR LONG-TERM PLANETARY GROWTH. A VERY PRAGMATIC VIEW TO TAKE.

"THE *ENTERPRISE* IS NOW *EN ROUTE* TO QAPMOC, AND MATTERS ARE NOW PROCEEDING IN A FAR MORE *ROUTINE, NORMAL* FASHION."

I DON'T *BELIEVE* IT--

--I JUST DON'T BELIEVE IT! I FOLDED ON THREE OF A KIND AND ALL YOU HAD WAS *GARBAGE*?!

IT WOULD *APPEAR* SO, MR. O'BRIEN. WELL DONE, AMBASSADOR!

BUT I *FOLDED* BECAUSE VULCANS NEVER *BLUFF!* THAT'S WHAT THE CAPTAIN SAID! THAT'S WHAT *YOU* SAID! THAT'S WHAT *EVERYBODY* SAID! VULCANS NEVER BLUFF!

THIS IS QUITE TRUE. VULCANS *NEVER* BLUFF--

--BUT THEY'VE *GOT* THE BEST *POKER* FACES IN THE GALAXY!

END

FOUR ISSUE
MINISERIES

STAR TREK:
THE MODALA
IMPERATIVE

2 US $1.75
CAN $2.25
UK £1

STAR TREK

THE MODALA IMPERATIVE ™

By MICHAEL JAN FRIEDMAN
AND PABLO MARCOS

ADAM 'N' KARL

FOUR ISSUE
MINISERIES

STAR TREK:
THE MODALA
IMPERATIVE

3

US $1.75
CAN $2.25
UK £1

STAR TREK

THE MODALA IMPERATIVE

STAR TREK
25 ANNIVERSARY

BY MICHAEL JAN FRIEDMAN
AND PABLO MARCOS

ADAM 'N' KARE

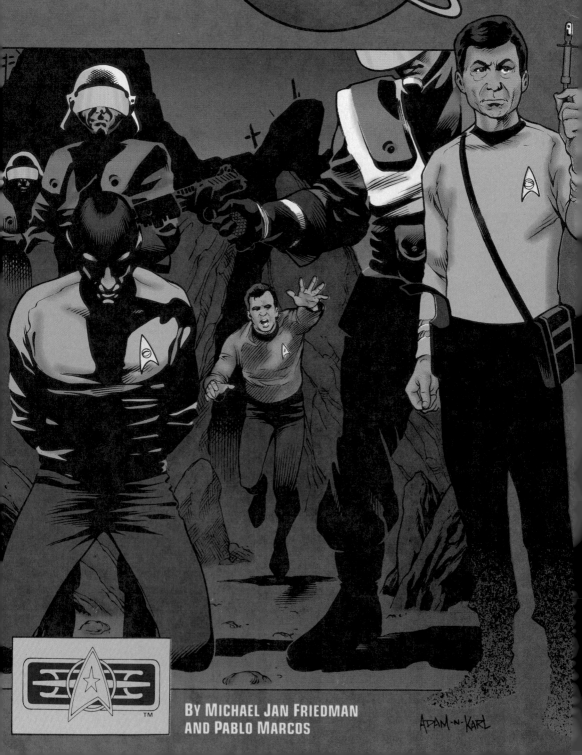

FOUR-ISSUE
MINISERIES

STAR TREK:
THE MODALA
IMPERATIVE

4

US $1.75
CAN $2.25
UK £1

STAR TREK

THE MODALA IMPERATIVE

BY MICHAEL JAN FRIEDMAN
AND PABLO MARCOS

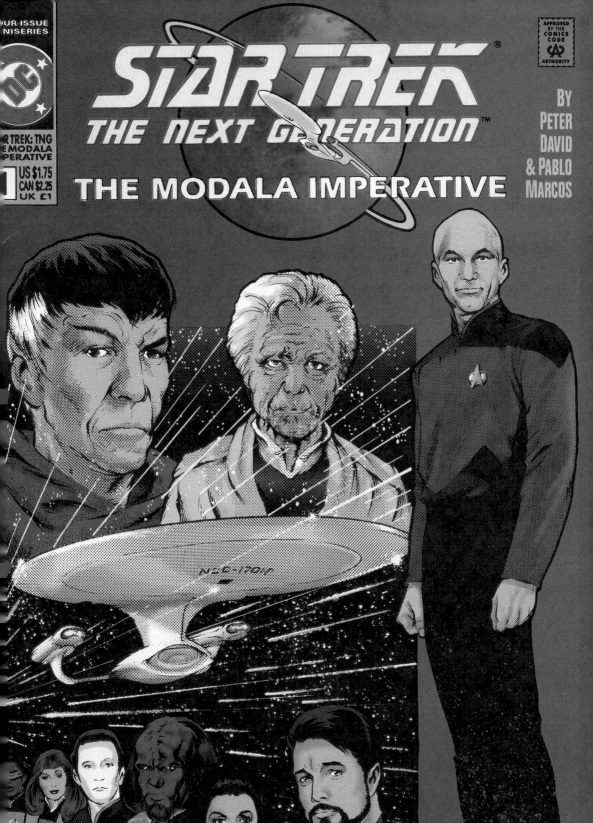

FOUR-ISSUE
MINISERIES

STAR TREK: TNG
THE MODALA
IMPERATIVE

4 US $1.75
CAN $2.25
UK £1

STAR TREK
THE NEXT GENERATION
THE MODALA IMPERATIVE

By PETER DAVID
& PABLO MARCOS

ADAM-N-KARL